The

VICT

HEROES

About the Authors

ADAM HART-DAVIS is the presenter of *Local Heroes* and *What the Victorians Did for Us*. A freelance writer and radio and television presenter since 1994, he previously worked for YTV as a researcher and producer, devising both *Scientific Eye*, the most successful school science series on television, and *Mathematical Eye* (1989–92). He is also a science photographer, and his photographs have appeared in a wide selection of publications. His books include *Thunder, Flush and Thomas Crapper* (1997), *The Local Heroes Book of British Ingenuity* (1997) and *Amazing Math Puzzles* (1998). He lives in Bristol, and travels by bicycle. . . .

PAUL BADER is the owner and managing director of Screenhouse Productions Limited, a television company which specialises in popular science programmes, and is producer and director of *Local Heroes* and *Science Shack*. He previously worked for YTV, producing medical, health and science programmes for the ITV network and Channel 4. Among other programmes, he has worked on *Discovery, The Buckman Treatment, The Halley's Comet Show* and *On the Edge*. He lives in Leeds, and travels by car.

The Book of VICTORIAN HEROES

ADAM HART-DAVIS
& PAUL BADER

SUTTON PUBLISHING

First published in 2001 by
Sutton Publishing Limited.
Parts of this book were first published in *The Local Heroes Book of British Ingenuity* (1997) and *More Local Heroes* (1998) by
Sutton Publishing Limited · Phoenix Mill
Thrupp · Stroud · Gloucestershire · GL5 2BU

British Library Cataloguing in Publication Data
A catalogue record for this book is available from the British Library.

ISBN 0-7509-2820-4

Cover illustrations, clockwise from left: Pedersen bicycle, ladies model (Gloucester Folk Museum); Garrett's steam-powered submarine, Resurgam; *Moule's earth-closet; Ada Lovelace (Mary Evans Picture Library); Ronald Ross; Adam Hart-Davis; Back: Muybridge horse series (Kingston Museum).*

Typeset in 11/14pt Photina.
Typesetting and origination by
Sutton Publishing Limited.
Printed and bound in England by
J.H. Haynes & Co. Ltd, Sparkford.

Contents

Foreword

Queen Victoria died in 1901, which makes the year 2001 a sensible year to celebrate some of the amazing achievements of her 64-year reign. When she came to the throne in 1837 the country had just recovered from the economic disaster of the Napoleonic wars, and the growing impact of the industrial revolution was immense. Britain was already the world leader in steam power, and in the production of iron and steel, and steadily increased her advantage during the next thirty years.

The new breed of scientists were discovering the secrets of electricity, and putting it to use, in chemistry, the telegraph, Alexander Graham Bell's telephone (with the Hunnings microphone), electric motors, and Swan's electric lights. Chemists were delivering new dyes, the first plastics, and the less exciting but equally important Portland cement.

Railway lines snaked across the country in the wake of Isambard Kingdom Brunel and Robert Stephenson; bridges of steel leaped across rivers and chasms; great ships steamed across the oceans; Joseph Paxton's Crystal Palace heralded a new era of construction; Eugenius Birch's piers strode out from the coastline into the sea; and there were minor triumphs too, such as the Pedrazzolli swimming umbrellas,

the Gaddes automatic egg boiler, and the Pullinger perpetual mousetrap.

There were tremendous improvements in health, brought about by such pioneers as Florence Nightingale, Ronald Ross, who discovered how malaria is transmitted, and Augustus Waller, with his electrocardiograph. In general, however, the Victorians were immensely proud of their growth and progress, confident in their knowledge of science and in their authority over the rest of the Empire and indeed the world. They were a self-made breed of scientific and technological heroes.

Adam Hart-Davis

Acknowledgements

The authors would like to thank the following individuals and organisations who generously provided illustrations for this book:

Bude & Stratton Town Museum, p. 11; Mary Evans Picture Library, pp. 28, 54, 84, 102, 126, 127; Henry Bessemer's autobiography, p. 68; Dorset County Museum, p. 77; Lincoln Central Library, pp. 94, 95; Leslie Herbert Gustar, p. 99; the Royal Society, p. 115; Kingston Museum, pp. 117, 119; Gloucester Folk Museum, p. 135; other pictures were provided by the authors.

Introduction

The Old Patent* Office in Bouverie Street, London, is one of our favourite haunts with its warren of stores and stacks holding the fruits of British invention. Although British law discourages monopolies, a patent gives inventors a brief period when they can exploit their idea free from competition, in exchange for telling the nation about it. The main patent office has long since decamped to Cardiff, to sleek new offices that reflect its role as a huge information-processing organisation, and that is certainly where you should go with your Improved Motorised Shoes or Windscreen Wipers for Bikes. But if like us you are interested in the history of British ingenuity, then getting your hands on the original patents from shelves full of leather-bound volumes has a certain magic. What is more, the patents from 1837 to 1901 encapsulate the explosion of science and engineering during the Victorian age.

At the start of her reign, Victoria would have been surprisingly aware of the patents taken out in Britain because every application required not only a visit to seven separate

* Curiously, normal pronunciation rules would have this as 'paytent' but the patent office say 'pattent'.

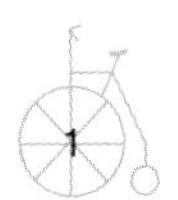

offices, but two signatures from the monarch. This discouraging process resulted in only 259 patent applications during her first year, despite this being the first age of the train. No doubt she would have been encouraged in 1839 when, the railway having been around for ten years, Thomas Edmondson finally invented the train ticket! We were particularly taken with two inventions from this early part of the reign – one surprising because it was invented so late, the other because it was years ahead of its time. In 1839 or 1840 (there are two commemorative plaques with different dates) Kirkpatrick MacMillan invented the bicycle. Why did it take so long? Surely the railway locomotive is more complicated, yet that was invented 36 years earlier. Also in 1840, at the time MacMillan was cycling the lanes of Dumfries, in the far north of Scotland Alexander Bain was inventing the fax machine. Yes, that is 1840, not 1940 or even 1960. Bain's story is one of the most surprising of any hero, and seems especially so when you stand as we did in the middle of a circular sheep-pen near John o'Groats, all that remains of the Bain family house.

The middle of the nineteenth century saw a revolution in Britain's attitude towards the inventor. It became clear that the painful process inventors went through (seven offices, two signatures from the queen) was holding them back, and might damage the nation. Two great events mark the change of heart: in 1851 the Great Exhibition celebrated trade and ingenuity, and in 1852 the patent system was reformed. The Exhibition, supported by Prince Albert, had an enormous impact; accounts of it crop up in the biographies of many of our heroes. The Crystal Palace itself encapsulates the spirit of the times. Its designer, Joseph Paxton, had been the gardener to the Duke of Devonshire, when he came up with an interesting system for building the glass-houses needed to house his employer's exotic water lilies. What is wonderful is that Paxton was in a position to think big, effectively inventing the first industrial building system. It is just as surprising that a 'mere' gardener got the job of designing the most important building in the country, apparently on merit alone.

The same decade as the Great Exhibition also saw a quite extraordinary, but at the time little celebrated, engineering feat in North Yorkshire, when Sir George Cayley launched the first ever heavier-than-air flying machine, his coachman at the controls. This was in fact the culmination of a career that had seen Cayley invent the science of aeronautics, for which he got handsome praise from Wilbur Wright after he and his brother made the first powered flight in 1903. At the time of his coachman's flight, Cayley would have been unknown outside a tiny circle of scientists, all of whom failed to share his vision of flight as the transport of the future. In October 1852, following the Great Exhibition and the Cayley flight, the new patent laws came in – and they worked. Between the January and October, a pathetic 464 applications for patents were made; from October to the end of the year there were 1,211. The age of the inventor had arrived.

It was as difficult then as now to predict which scientific ideas would be important. The Victorians didn't have their lives changed by flight, but other work had an immediate impact. In 1854 Florence Nightingale shamed the nation into caring about sanitation and disease, which were carrying off

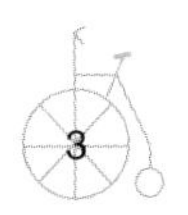

up to seven times as many troops fighting in the Crimean War as were killed in battle. But in the same year Henry Bessemer, pioneer of steel production, no doubt thought his 'anti-seasickness boat' would prove terribly useful. It was a complete and rather spectacular flop.

The top Victorian year for patent applications was 1897 with over 30,000 – remember there were just 259 in the first year of the reign. By this point we have already had such crucial inventions for modern life as Alexander Graham Bell's telephone in 1876, Joseph Swan's electric light bulb in 1879, and Dunlop's version of the pneumatic tyre in 1888. There are a lot of bicycle inventions, including a bike made from bamboo and the elegant Petersen machines held together with string. But the end of the century seems to have been marked by an outbreak of silliness, the 1890s boasting devices like the automatic egg boiler invented by a Harrogate dentist, and the 'swimming umbrellas' of Liborio Pedrazzolli, proof that anyone could get into the inventing game.

Our memories of these inventions are often coloured by what happened when we tried to recreate them for the *Local Heroes* television series. In Hackney Baths it became immediately clear why Signor Pedrazzolli had not made a fortune from his umbrellas, intended to help you get a grip on the water and swim like a fish. A drowning fish, perhaps. The celebration of Crystal Palace builder Joseph Paxton was at the beautiful Chatsworth House, seat of the Dukes of Devonshire, where he worked. We had constructed a home-made water lily pad, to show where Paxton got his engineering inspiration, and successfully floated Adam on it. Part two was a miniature crystal palace. In the middle of filming, the

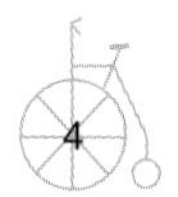

heavens opened and we retreated to the van to wait for a dry spell, leaving the 'palace' unattended. As we watched a substantial crowd gathered, wondering if our creation in drain pipe, wood and plastic sheeting was perhaps an artistic installation. Other memories are more moving. Florence Nightingale was the first to use statistics to make a medical argument, and invented the forerunner of the pie chart to show what was really happening in the Crimean War. As Adam recited the figures, it brought home the appalling conditions young British soldiers were subject to, and how cheaply their lives were lost. Later that day we went to Florence's gravestone, marked not with her name but with a simple 'F.N.' because she did not want to be treated as a hero.

Given a time-travel machine, there are a few periods in 'Hero History' we would like to visit. The time of Isaac Newton and the founding of the Royal Society is certainly one, but the Victorian era must be another, since it is the high-water mark of British invention. We hope this book gives you a flavour of what such a trip might be like.

Paul Bader

Just the Ticket! Thomas Edmondson

Some inventions look so obvious with the benefit of hindsight that it seems extraordinary that they took so long to appear. A good example is the printed railway ticket. Railways began to provide serious transport in the early 1830s, and to start with every ticket was written out on paper by hand and every passenger's name written down in a big book in the booking office. This was a laborious business, and for any complex journey distributing the money was a nightmare, since there were more than fifty different railway companies.

The breakthrough came in 1837 at Brampton, 12 miles east of Carlisle, where the railway station was built a mile and a half out of town so that it would not interfere with the horse trade. The man with the vision was the stationmaster, Thomas Edmondson.

Edmondson was born in Lancaster on 30 June 1792. He was always fiddling with things, and when he was a small boy his mother, seeing that he could never be kept out of mischief, taught him to knit so that he would at least be quiet and useful. Later he connected the baby's cradle to the butter churn, so that when anyone was making butter they rocked

Edmondson was ticket-clerk at Brampton when he had the idea for his ticket system.

the baby at the same time. He became a cabinet-maker and went into business in Carlisle, but it failed, and he became bankrupt.

So at the age of forty-four he joined the Newcastle & Carlisle Railway and became stationmaster at Brampton – and had to suffer all the inefficiency of manual ticketing. One day, walking across a field, he had a vision: the process could be mechanised. Tickets could be printed for particular journeys, numbered, dated, and finally clipped when they'd been used. The whole system apparently came to him in one single flash of inspiration.

Unfortunately the Newcastle & Carlisle Railway said there would be no demand. Luckily for Edmondson – and us – in 1839 the brand new Manchester & Leeds Railway offered to double his salary if he would go and work for them and introduce his system. Within a few years it was in use not only throughout Britain but all over the world. And his system was so effective and so simple that it wasn't bettered for 150 years – until computers came along.

He did well from his invention, by patenting it and charging a royalty of 10*s* per mile per annum – in other words any railway company using his system paid him 10*s* a year for every mile of track; so if they had 30 miles of track they paid him £15 a year. And according to the history books 'he worked out his invention with skill and patience, enjoyed its honours with modesty, and dispensed its fruits with generosity'.

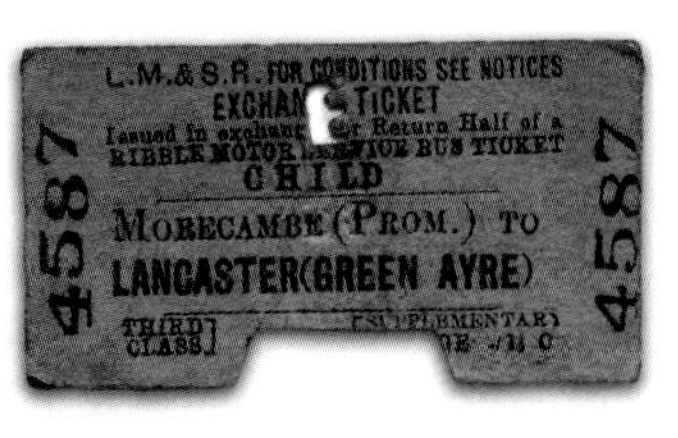

An Edmondson-style railway ticket, numbered by his special machine.

Trains still stop at Brampton station, although it now has neither buildings nor a stationmaster.

Goldsworthy Gurney: Bright Light, and Exhausting Hot Air

Candles and gas lamps produced a feeble, yellowish, flickering glow, just about bright enough to read by, but hardly enough to fill a large room with light. The first really bright light was invented by a Cornishman called Goldsworthy Gurney. He was an enterprising and energetic man, who was born on 14 February 1793 at Padstow, had a medical practice before he was twenty, married a farmer's daughter the next year, and moved to London in 1820. Thereafter he divided his time between London, where he could be part of Society, and the

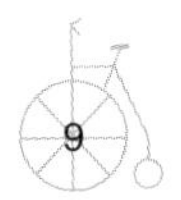

north Cornish seaside town of Bude, where in the early 1830s he built himself a castle. It's still there, standing on a concrete raft on a sand dune, close to where the canal empties on to the beach.

Allegedly he lit the whole of his castle with a single central lamp, reflecting light into every room with carefully placed mirrors. This was clever, but what was really revolutionary was the light itself, for it was far brighter than any lamp had been before. Gurney achieved this by blowing oxygen into the flame, thus ensuring rapid and complete combustion of the fuel. In 1823 he had been awarded the Isis gold medal of the Royal Society of Arts for his invention of the oxygen-hydrogen blowpipe, and his 'Bude Light' was really just a practical extension of the same idea, though he did not patent it until 1839.

Bude Lights were used to brighten the streets of London – notably Trafalgar Square and Pall Mall – and in 1839 Gurney was invited to improve the lighting in the House of Commons. He did so in a dramatically simple way, by removing 280 candles, and replacing them with just three Bude Lights, which successfully lit the place for sixty years, until electricity came along around the turn of the century. But Gurney's bright thoughts went further than this, for in 1864 he wrote a paper outlining how seamen might identify lighthouses; he proposed that each lighthouse should have a Bude Light in a revolving frame, so that from anywhere out at sea it would flash on and off at regular intervals. By varying the number of flashes and the intervals between them, each lighthouse could have its own signature; thus a sailor who was sailing along the coast at night could quickly work out his exact position. Now, for example, the Eddystone Lighthouse shows two flashes every ten seconds, while the Bishop Rock Lighthouse shows two flashes every fifteen seconds.

Gurney's most spectacular invention – and the one that cost him most money – was the steam carriage. He had come up with the idea of the high-pressure steam jet, probably as yet another by-product of the oxygen-hydrogen jet, which greatly increased the efficiency of steam engines, and was apparently adopted by the Stephensons in their famous locomotives. Gurney, however, decided to use it to build a steam carriage, which he patented in 1825. He simply removed the horses from the front of an ordinary coach, and replaced them with a steam engine. At first he put the boiler under the passenger seats, but realised this might inspire terror, and in 1828 designed and built a Drag – a separate engine to pull the coach.

Goldsworthy Gurney's steam carriage.

He gave up his successful medical practice in 1826 to develop the Gurney Steam Carriage Company, and in November 1827 the *Gentleman's Magazine* announced 'A steam-coach company is now making arrangements for stopping places on the line of road between London, Bath, and Bristol, which will occur every six or seven miles, where fresh fuel and water are to be supplied. There are fifteen coaches built.'

In 1829 Gurney was asked by the Quartermaster-General of the Army to lay on an official demonstration, in the shape of a journey from London to Bath and back. They set off at the dead of night on 27 July for what proved to be quite an adventure. After less than a mile, while crossing over a temporary bridge, they managed to collide with the Bristol mail-coach, and had to repair the damage in Reading. They were attacked by a Luddite mob in Melksham and had to cover the last few miles to Bath under guard. After four days' rest they returned home, completing the round trip at an average speed of 15 mph, much faster than the mail-coach. This was the first long journey at a maintained speed by any mechanised vehicle.

Two weeks later, on 12 August, the Duke of Wellington, then Prime Minister, asked for a demonstration in Hounslow Barracks, where the Drag first pulled the duke's carriage around the yard, and later a wagon carrying twenty-seven soldiers.

Sir Charles Dance started a regular steam carriage service between Cheltenham and Gloucester – covering the 9 miles four times a day – which ran for five months in 1831 until it was sabotaged by the mail-coach owners. However, despite this and other triumphs, the steam carriage failed to carry

the day. The government decided to back the rapidly developing railways with an Exchequer Loan of £100,000, but rushed through a series of Turnpike Bills which put prohibitive tolls on horseless carriages. Gurney protested, and petitioned Parliament, but in 1832 his business failed; he had to abandon the whole thing, and lost £232,000.

One thing Gurney must have known as well as anyone was that politicians produce a great deal of hot air. In the 1850s MPs kept falling asleep, and in 1854 Gurney was appointed Inspector of Ventilation at the Houses of Parliament. He sorted them out with one of his steam jets, and went on to develop the Gurney Stove for warming and moisturising air; it was used in many cathedrals.

His steam jets were also used to put out a fire in a coal mine at Clackmannan that had been burning for thirty years, and to clean out a revolting sewer at Friar Street.

In 1863 he was knighted by Queen Victoria, and twelve years later he died. His daughter, a fanatical supporter, donated a memorial chiming clock to the church at Poughill on the north side of Bude. It's a pretty stone church, with chickens in the graveyard, the nice blue clock on the tower, and a strong bell-ringing tradition. There's an excellent plaque inside the church above the door, describing with only slight exaggeration why he was a hero: 'His inventions and discoveries in steam and electricity rendered transport by land and sea so rapid that it became necessary for all England to keep uniform clock time.'

Goldsworthy Gurney's castle is now Bude Town Hall.

Kirkpatrick MacMillan and the First Pedal-powered Bicycle

Courthill Smithy in the parish of Keir, about 14 miles from Dumfries, has more plaques on it than the average blacksmith's premises, and amazingly they all claim that right there Kirkpatrick MacMillan invented the bicycle. It is rather surprising to find that one person invented the bike, and more so that the invention came so late – in 1839, ten years after Stephenson's *Rocket* and thirty-five years after the first steam locomotives. What's more, tricycles were around in 1828. But did MacMillan really do it?

Macmillan's bike was hard enough to ride down the road, never mind to Glasgow where he had the first ever traffic accident involving a bicycle.

Kirkpatrick MacMillan was born in Keir in September 1812, and became a blacksmith like his dad. He probably went off to work on a neighbouring farm, got a job as a coachman, and at twenty-two became an assistant to the blacksmith of the Duke of Buccleuch. Eventually he returned to Courthill to assist his father and took over the business when his dad retired in 1851.

The story of the bicycle is a bit more complicated. Some people think it went like this: in Germany Karl von Drais had invented the hobby-horse in 1817. It had no pedals, so you sat astride it and pushed with your feet on the ground and scooted along. This was a big craze for a few years, and it is quite possible that MacMillan saw one of these machines. Later, in the 1860s, pedal-driven bicycles were made by Michaux in Paris and were known as bone-shakers or velocipedes, depending on whether you were more impressed by their comfort or by their speed. The 'ordinary', high bicycle or penny-farthing came along in about 1870. But according to supporters of the Courthill blacksmith, Kirkpatrick MacMillan built the first powered bicycle much earlier, in 1839.

At this time the only bicycle around was the hobby-horse, and MacMillan's brilliant realisation was that it would actually be better to power the machine via some sort of mechanism, rather than using the feet directly on the ground. So MacMillan's machine was wooden like a hobby-horse. It had wooden wheels with solid tyres but with a treadle-powered crank mechanism acting on the rear wheel. This consisted of two iron rods (he was an ironmonger, after all) hinged from just below the handlebar, one on each side. At the bottom of the rods were the pedals, which in turn were connected to the rear wheel cranks by a second pair of iron rods.

Riding it feels pretty peculiar to someone used to a modern bike – it's more like a foot-powered sewing machine. You have to get it rolling, and then push the pedals forwards, away from you, rather than downwards. It feels very heavy and steering is quite difficult because the cranks restrict the movement of the front wheel. Apparently the original machine weighed half a hundredweight, but in spite of this MacMillan frequently rode into Dumfries in less than an hour, which is impressive, to say the least. But it is without question a powered bicycle.

The critics say it is not the precursor of the modern bike. Drive to the back wheels didn't come into serious use for another forty years, and the treadles were a blind alley. However, we are used to pioneers who were ahead of their time. The more serious question concerns the evidence. And there isn't much evidence that MacMillan really built and rode such a machine – except a wonderful article in the *Glasgow Argus* of 1842 which reports that a gentleman of Dumfriesshire had ridden a velocipede 40 miles from Old Cumnock to Glasgow in five hours, and there among a crowd of spectators had mounted the pavement and knocked over a small child. Luckily the child was unhurt and the gentleman was fined only five shillings.

Unfortunately the article does not mention MacMillan by name, nor does it say that the velocipede was a bicycle, and by the social standards of the day he was not a gentleman. And it does say the wheels were turned by *hand*. On the other hand, in the area round Courthill, MacMillan's claim is recognised.

He didn't bother to patent the design and indeed seems to have done little with it, but others saw his bike, copied it and sold the copies for £6 or £7. Apparently Gavin Dalzell of Lesmahagow copied the MacMillan machine in 1846, and his design became so well known that for years *he* was regarded as the inventor of the bicycle! So there is some controversy about who actually invented the bicycle. If it was Kirkpatrick MacMillan, the blacksmith of Courthill, he should surely be saluted as a mechanical genius who in the age of steam was the first to harness human power in a vehicle.

Courthill smithy is now a private house, albeit with plaques on the wall. It stands a few miles south-west of Thornhill. There is a replica of the MacMillan bike in the Bicycle Museum, Drumlanrig Castle.

Alexander Bain and the Fax Machine

The telephone was invented in 1875 by a Scotsman in America, and the instrument has utterly changed our lives. The fax machine brought about another substantial change when it came into general use in about the 1970s. I was astonished to discover that the fax machine was actually patented thirty years before the telephone was invented, by an ingenious shepherd from the north of Scotland called Alexander Bain.

The stones of the Bain family home at Leanmore, near Wick, have been made into a circular sheep-pen. Part of the original floor is still in place.

Alexander Bain and his twin sister Margaret were born in October 1810. Their dad was a crofter, and he had six sisters and six brothers. They grew up in a remote stone cottage at Leanmore, a few miles north of Wick. The vast expanse of peaty countryside has only occasional scattered cottages, and the Bain house, close to a small wood, became a sheep byre, and is now little more than an outline of low stone walls. In the winter Sandy walked a mile or two to school in Backlass; in the summer he worked as a shepherd.

He was bottom of his class in school, and was a poor shepherd too, because he was always dreaming. But he was fascinated by clocks, and actually made himself a model clock using heather for the spring and the cogwheels, so his sympathetic father got him apprenticed to a clockmaker in Wick.

In January 1830 he walked 21 miles through the snow from Wick to Thurso to hear a lecture on 'Light, heat, and the electric fluid'. The lecture changed his life, for he decided then and there that electricity was the stuff to work with. He began inventing electrical devices, including various types of automatic telegraph, an electric clock, an earth battery, insulation for electric cables and an electric fire alarm. He took out patents on all these, and also on inkstands, inkholders and a ship's log. The most amazing idea he had was for what he called the electro-chemical telegraph, which we would call a fax machine. However, before he had a chance to develop it, he ran into an unpleasant spot of trouble in London.

In 1840 Bain was desperate for money to develop his clocks and his fax machine; he talked about his financial problems to the editor of the *Mechanics Magazine*, who introduced him to the well-known and highly respected Professor Sir Charles Wheatstone. Bain took his models to demonstrate at Wheatstone's house.

Wheatstone watched Bain's gadgets with fascination, and then, when asked for his opinion, said 'Oh, I shouldn't bother to develop these things any further! There's no future in them.' Bain went away disconsolate, but three months later Wheatstone went to the Royal Society and before the leaders of the scientific establishment demonstrated an electric clock, claiming it was his own invention. Luckily, Bain had already applied for his patent.

Professor Sir Charles Wheatstone had all the advantages of rank and social position, and did his level best to block Bain's patents. He failed, and rumours of his skulduggery began to circulate. So when Wheatstone organised an Act of Parliament to set up the Electric Telegraph Company, the House of Lords summoned Bain to give evidence, and eventually compelled the company to pay Bain £10,000 and give him a job as manager. Wheatstone resigned in a huff.

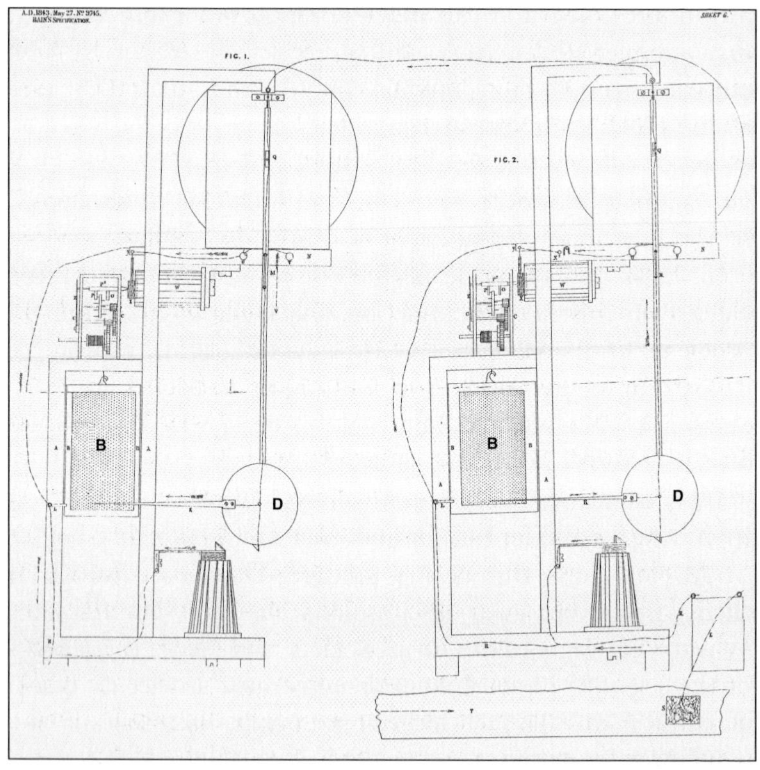

Part of Bain's 'Electro-chemical telegraph' – his fax machine. The pendulum 'D' scanned back and forth as the metal picture 'B' was dropped down. A similar machine at the other end drew a picture on electrically sensitive paper.

In 1841 Sandy Bain made a new kind of electric telegraph, the first of three devices he dreamed up to send pictures or printed words along telegraph wires. This was an idea decades ahead of its time: in those days messages were sent by Morse code – people had to wait thirty years for the telephone – so even a skilled operator could send only a few words a minute. Bain's machine was to change all that.

Bain had already worked out how to set up a system of clocks that would remain exactly synchronised. He put a master clock in the railway station in Edinburgh, and another clock in the railway station in Glasgow. Then he arranged that every time the Edinburgh pendulum swung it sent a pulse of electricity along the telegraph wires, which drove a solenoid in Glasgow and pushed the Glasgow pendulum at exactly the same time. Bain's electrical mechanism didn't just make the clocks run at the same rate, it forced the pendulums to stay precisely in step.

When he wanted to send a picture along the wires, he made a copy of it in copper, and etched away everything but the lines he wanted. Then he arranged for a metal needle or stylus to swing across the picture. Each time it touched copper it made contact and sent a pulse along the telegraph wire.

The needle was attached to the pendulum of the clock at each end, so the positions of the contacts were faithfully reproduced at the receiving end by a matching stylus running across electro-sensitive paper; whenever there was a blip of current the stylus left a black mark on the paper, corresponding to the position of the line in the original picture.

Finally he arranged for both pictures – the one being sent and the one being received – to drop down by a millimetre at every swing of the pendulum. Thus the outgoing picture was gradually scanned by the stylus swinging across it and moving down line by line, and at the receiving end the new copy picture was gradually built up.

The whole concept was an outstanding example of pushing the available technology to its limits. Unfortunately, Bain, despite his ingenuity, was hopeless with money. He wasted lots in litigation in America, and lots more on trying to achieve perpetual motion. He eventually died in Glasgow, poor and sad, in 1877.

Wheatstone is famous, Bain is forgotten. But the man who invented the fax machine, a vital feature of every office today, was that unknown shepherd from Caithness, Alexander Bain.

The main Telecom building in Thurso is called the Alexander Bain Building, and there is an original Bain electric clock in the hall at Watten, between Wick and Thurso.

William Coppin and the *Great Northern*

For thousands of years boats have been built of wood, and although one or two were made of iron in the eighteenth century, large iron ships were not built until the 1840s. One of the most famous was Brunel's *Great Britain*, but the first of the large iron ships was the *Great Northern*, built in Northern Ireland by Captain William Coppin.

William Coppin was born in County Cork on 9 October 1805, twelve days before the Battle of Trafalgar, and the sea was in his blood. At the age of fifteen he rescued six customs men when their boat capsized in the River Shannon, and when he finished school his parents sent him off to Canada to learn about boat-building.

He came back to Ireland and built a 100-ton ship – the *Kathleen* – when he was only twenty-four. Then he was commissioned to build a 600-tonner, the *Edward Reid*. He delivered it himself to a timber merchant in Londonderry. He loved the place so much that a few years later he went back to live there.

Coppin was a good sailor, and captained a number of other ships in the next eight years, including paddle-steamers to Philadelphia and passenger ships to Liverpool, before buying a boatyard on the River Foyle below the soaring battlements of Londonderry. There he built many ships, of every size and kind. The most spectacular, and the most famous, was the *Great Northern*, which was launched on 23 July 1842. At 220 feet long, and with a displacement of 1,750 tons, she was the biggest ship ever built in Ireland. She was rigged as a 50-gun frigate. She had three masts, and carried a full set of square-rigged sails, and a huge 370 horse-power steam engine which drove an Archimedes screw propeller, 12 feet in diameter, thundering round at a

Captain William Coppin (1805–95).

stately 88 rpm. The launch was such an event that twenty thousand spectators gathered to watch, crammed on every bit of dock, on the rooftops, and on sixty boats offshore. Even the Donegal Grand Jury insisted on coming, and the court was closed for the day!

Coppin sailed her round to London, because he hoped to sell her to the British government. Unfortunately this was the only voyage the *Great Northern* ever made, for after a long and expensive delay, while Coppin sat in dock biting his nails, the British government said 'No thanks'; perhaps they thought it would be unwise to buy a warship from Ireland. Coppin, now almost bankrupt, had to sell the ship for scrap to pay the harbour dues.

In his later life Coppin turned to salvage. Lots of ships sank, and in deep water they were extremely hard to reach. But they often had on board not only valuable cargo, but expensive steam engines, well worth recovering. So William Coppin thought hard about how to get down to the wrecks and bring them up. In 1876 he patented an amazing new diving suit. It was revolutionary in two ways: when you dive down more than a few feet in the sea, you are subjected to great pressure – go down to 30 feet and you have double the pressure at the surface, at 60 feet, three times the pressure, and so on. Coppin's new diving suit had two waterproof rubber skins, separated by tough ribs that would withstand some of this extra pressure, and so make life easier for the diver. It was the first attempt at a partially armoured suit. He also invented a better system for breathing out. Before then, divers had had to exhale straight into the water, which meant they had to breathe out against all that pressure. Coppin's

William Coppin's *Great Northern* made just one voyage.

new suit brought the used air back to the surface, so he could control the pressure at which they breathed out. With his brilliant new equipment, Coppin claimed he could go down to 120 feet and stay there for an hour – which was a great advance on what had been possible before.

He developed a cunning technique – to plug all the holes in a boat with clay, and then fill the hull with air, so that it floated to the surface. Coppin had realised that bubbles of air under water have immense lifting power. Archimedes' Principle says that the uplift is equal to the weight of water displaced. So if you fill a large ship with air when it's under water, the uplift should be almost a ton for every cubic metre – more than enough to float the ship to the surface!

Coppin was a prolific inventor. In 1886 he patented an electric fish-catching apparatus – which looks like a winner, if you can believe the picture on the box!

However, the strangest Coppin tale is not about the captain, but concerns his young daughter Louisa, known to the family as 'Weesy'. She was born in 1846, and died on 27 May 1849, aged only three and a half. Six months later a ball of bluish light appeared in one room of the house. Curiously, the other children weren't frightened; they said it was just Weesy, come back to visit them. They used to chat to Weesy's ghost, and ask it questions. One day they asked what had happened to Sir John Franklin, the great explorer, who had gone off past Newfoundland to look for the north-west passage to India. He had set sail two years earlier with the ships *Erebus* and *Terror*, and no trace of the expedition had been seen since. The blue ball of light apparently produced a map on the wall, which showed the whereabouts of the ships and the expedition. Coppin noted the details and in May 1850 went to see Lady Franklin, who was so convinced that she launched another expedition to search for them in the spot identified by Weesy's ghost.

William Coppin's grave is in St Augustine's churchyard, high up near the battlements of Londonderry. His home down the hill at Ivy House – 34 Strand Road – has become a pizza restaurant.

Ada Lovelace's Computer Program

Augusta Ada Byron was born on 10 December 1815 in Piccadilly, the only child of that great romantic poet and seducer of women, George Gordon, Lord Byron – 'mad, bad, and dangerous to know' – and Anne Isabella Milbanke. When she was four months old, her parents divorced very publicly. She never saw her father again, although he wrote about her in *Childe Harold*:

Is thy face like thy mother's, my fair child
Ada, sole daughter of my house and of my heart?
When last I saw thy young blue eyes they smiled,
And then we parted – not as now we part,
But with a hope.

Ada spent most of her life at 10 St James's Square, in the heart of London. She married the future Lord Lovelace in 1835. Her mother was a mathematician – Byron called her the 'Princess of Parallelograms' – and she made sure Ada was trained in mathematics.

In 1833 Ada met Charles Babbage, and was fascinated by his ideas for calculating machines. In a lecture in Turin he proudly announced his plans and dreams for the analytical engine. In 1842 this lecture was written up in French by General Menabrea. Ada translated his paper into English, and at Babbage's suggestion began to add her own notes about how the analytical engine might be used. In the end her notes were three times as long as the original paper, and they

Ada Lovelace: brains, beauty and a disastrous private life.

provide the best information we have about the potential of the analytical engine.

Ada's notes explained how Babbage's analytical engine would have taken instructions on punched cards, in what we now call a program. She described the 'store' or memory, and the 'mill' or central processing unit, and she speculated about what the machine might be capable of; it would not produce original ideas, she said, but it would greatly help the advance of science, and it might be helpful in composing music, she thought. She clearly had a vision of the future, and would have loved the computers of today.

Most important of all, she described in detail exactly what instructions the analytical engine would need in order to perform various complex mathematical calculations. We don't know how much of this was her work, and how much Babbage's, since they certainly collaborated, but she was the first person to write

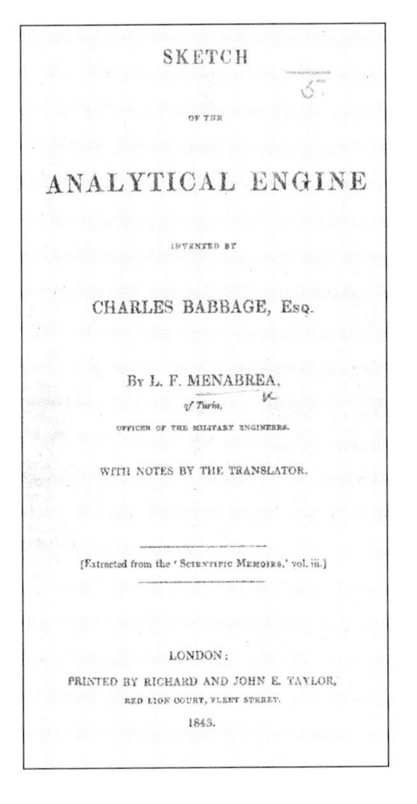
SKETCH

OF THE

ANALYTICAL ENGINE

INVENTED BY

CHARLES BABBAGE, ESQ.

BY L. F. MENABREA,

of Turin,

OFFICER OF THE MILITARY ENGINEERS.

WITH NOTES BY THE TRANSLATOR.

[Extracted from the 'SCIENTIFIC MEMOIRS,' vol. iii.]

LONDON:

PRINTED BY RICHARD AND JOHN E. TAYLOR,

RED LION COURT, FLEET STREET.

1843.

The first computer program? Ada Lovelace's detailed ideas on how a computer might be programmed could easily be missed – the publisher described them as 'notes by the translator'.

it down, and she can therefore reasonably be described as the world's first computer programmer!

Ada had tremendous ambition. She believed she would be able to work out the mathematics of the brain; she may perhaps have heard of George Boole's 1833 vision about the mathematics of the mind, which eventually became his book *The Laws of Thought* (1854), and the foundation of Boolean algebra. She wrote to Babbage: 'The more I study, the more irresistible do I feel my genius to be.' But her life was tragic. She ran up terrible debts, possibly from gambling, but it seems from letters found after her death that she was being blackmailed by John Crosse, with whom she probably had a discreet affair. After she died they found she had even pawned her husband's family jewels. And the world's first computer programmer died from cancer at the age of thirty-six.

Ada Lovelace's birthplace in Piccadilly has become a delicatessen, but her home at 10 St James's Square, now elegant offices, is marked with a blue plaque.

James Nasmyth: Hammers in his Blood

Perhaps the most basic of all engineering tools is the hammer. The basic principle is always the same: it's a bit of iron on a stick that you hit things with. But Karl Marx noted that in Birmingham at one time over 500 different types of hammer were made. So for a man to revolutionise such a venerable tool is quite an achievement – and James Nasmyth did exactly that. He was, moreover, a self-made and educated man in the tradition of great British engineers.

Nasmyth was the son of an Edinburgh artist. Although he went to school, his education has been called 'desultory'. The problem seems to have been that fathers of friends owned a chemical works and an iron foundry, and young James spent as much time there as at school. But by the time he was a teenager, he was accomplished in working metal. He used to practise casting brass secretly at night, having converted the fireplace in his bedroom into a furnace. Unfortunately he often woke his father, sleeping in the bedroom below, with the sound of tapping down sand in the mould. He soon solved the problem by putting some old carpet under the mould. Clearly nothing was going to stop him becoming an engineer.

James achieved a considerable local reputation by the time he was nineteen, when he was commissioned by the Scottish Society of Arts to make a working steam carriage that could carry twelve people. Apparently the carriage was a familiar sight on the streets of Edinburgh in 1827 or '28 – a year before Stephenson's *Rocket*. Many people might have been satisfied at that, but James knew that he had more to learn. He had heard that Henry Maudslay was the greatest engineer in Britain, and was determined to work for him. Maudslay is now regarded as one of the founders of production-line engineering, having collaborated with Marc Brunel in making a series of machines to take over production of all the blocks (pulleys used on ships) for the Navy.

So Nasmyth travelled to Maudslay's works at Lambeth in south London (the site is now Lambeth North tube station) and took along a model steam engine he had made. He was taken on immediately as assistant in Maudslay's private workshop. After two years in London, James wanted to set up on his own, and returned to Edinburgh. It was here that he really lived up to the title 'self-made man'. With no capital, he could not afford machine tools – and in any case did not want machines made by someone else. Instead he spent two years making all the tools needed for an engineering business. He started with just chisels and a lump of iron, from which he made a superb lathe. He then used the lathe to construct everything else.

His ambition to be at the centre of great engineering took him in 1834 to Manchester where he rented space in a building in Dale Street. The factory soon had a tremendous reputation for machine tools, but also made engines. Indeed one of these led indirectly to the expansion of the business when it crashed through the floor and into the glassworks below! The landlord was less than impressed and suggested that Nasmyth might like to look for larger premises elsewhere. Curiously, he already had somewhere in mind. A few years previously he had travelled from London to Liverpool to see the *Rocket* in action. Like any decent self-made engineer, he had decided to walk and on the return journey paused for a rest. The spot he had chosen was at Patricroft, outside Manchester and next to the Bridgewater Canal. At the time he had thought what a wonderful site this would make for an engineering works, and now set about making his vision a reality. The Bridgewater Foundry eventually earned a world-

Nasmyth's steam hammer.

wide reputation, and included among its clients Isambard Kingdom Brunel (son of Marc), making locomotives for his Great Western Railway.

It was a failed Brunel contract that led to Nasmyth's most famous invention. The steamship the *Great Britain* was to be driven by enormous paddle wheels, and the Bridgewater Foundry got the contract for the paddle shaft. But Nasmyth realised immediately that something new was required: this was a far larger piece of forging than had ever been undertaken. He took out his 'scheme book' where he sketched the plans for his new tools, and later wrote: 'In little more than half an hour after receiving Mr Humphries' letter . . . I had the whole contrivance in all its details before me in a page of my scheme book.'

Forging is essentially the blacksmith's art. Metal, heated until it becomes soft, is worked by bashing and bending it into shape. But as the shafts, pistons and wheels of the steam age became larger they became more difficult to work. The 'helve' hammer was often used, essentially a huge conventional hammer pivoted at the end of the shaft. The head was raised by a crank, driven by hand or an engine, and allowed to fall on the piece being worked. But with a big piece of iron, the hammer remained near the top of its travel, and its impact was both feeble and at an angle. Nasmyth invented the steam hammer. He connected the head of the hammer directly to the piston of a steam engine. The head was to be raised vertically by injecting steam under the piston, and then allowed to fall.

The beauty of the new hammer was that it could be precisely controlled. Unlike the old helve hammer, you could vary the height to which the hammer was raised, and this was all done simply by opening or closing a steam valve: 5 tons under fingertip control. Except that the new hammer was never made. Screw propellers became the latest thing in marine power, were adopted for the *Great Britain*, and the huge paddle shaft was no longer needed. The plans remained in the scheme book as a curiosity.

Then in 1842 Nasmyth was visiting the Creuzot foundry in France, and noticed how excellent their big forgings were. He asked how they had been made: the answer astounded him. The huge forgings in France had been made with his steam hammer! The chief engineer at Creuzot had visited Patricroft while Nasmyth was away, had been shown the plans in the scheme book, and pinched the idea for himself. Although the hammer had already been patented in France, Nasmyth lost no time in making one at Patricroft and taking out the British patent for himself.

James Nasmyth's is a story very much of his time. He had the vision to see that what the fledgling engineering industry needed was both great precision and mass production at the same time, and produced the tools to make this possible. When he retired it was to Kent and a house he called Hammerfield because (he claimed) of his 'hereditary regard for hammers, two broken hammer-shafts having been the crest of the family for hundreds of years'.

The museum of Science and Industry in Manchester is a wonderful celebration of Victorian science in the north-west. it is on Liverpool Road, Castlefield, in the city centre and is open 10–5 daily except 24, 25 and 26 December. Information line: 0161 832 1830.

The First Powered Flight, by John Stringfellow

People have always wanted to fly. The ancients imagined gods and angels soaring through the heavens, and created such legends as that of Daedalus and Icarus, who made wings from feathers stuck on with wax. In the eighteenth century

hot-air balloonists took to the skies, but not until the middle of the nineteenth century were successful flights made by machines that were heavier than air.

Most people think the aeroplane was invented by Orville and Wilbur Wright. In fact, the world's first powered flight took place not in America in 1903 but at Chard in Somerset fifty-five years earlier, and the man who made it happen was John Stringfellow.

Stringfellow was born in Attercliffe, on the outskirts of Sheffield, on 6 December 1799. When he was a teenager his family moved to Nottingham, and he went into the lace industry, becoming a bobbin and carriage maker – which meant essentially a precision engineer. The lace trade suffered badly from the Luddite riots, and some lace-makers decided to move to the calmer county of Somerset. John Stringfellow became the leading bobbin and carriage maker in Chard.

John Stringfellow (1799–1883).

In 1827 he married American Hannah Keetch; they settled in Combe Street and had ten children, number four being John – always known as Fred – who wrote the only eyewitness account of his father's work.

John Stringfellow lectured on electricity to the Chard Institution, and in 1831 he launched a hot-air balloon to celebrate the coronation of William IV. He developed amazing skill at making steam engines. In about 1842 he teamed up with

William Samuel Henson, an aeronautics enthusiast, and they began to discuss how to fly. They worried about what shape the wings of a plane should be, and how light it would have to be. They reckoned it would be sensible to use birds as models, so they took a muzzle-loading duck gun and shot all kinds of birds, which they weighed and measured, trying to find some mathematical connection between weight and wing dimensions. Eventually they settled on the rook: 'Henson and me generally took the rook as our standard as carrying half a pound to a foot. This bird can be seen any day leisurely flying at a speed not more than 20 miles an hour, and we considered that if we kept our machine within these limits we had a fair chance of success.'

Their basic idea was this. Take any wing – a bit like a bird's – keep it at an angle and push it through the air, and it will generate lift. Stringfellow once shot a square of cardboard across the room, saying, 'Any surface will hold the air with applied power.' This is interesting; most people didn't believe you could apply power to a surface and make it fly. They thought the wings of an aircraft would have to flap, like a bird's.

Stringfellow used to go up to London to visit Henson, and used the train journey to do experiments with the lift generated by various surfaces; he would lean out of the window and gauge the lift of wings held in the airstream.

Henson was tremendously ambitious. In 1842 he not only applied for a patent for a 'Locomotive Apparatus for Air, Land, and Water' but also tried to set up an airline! The patent drawings show a monoplane with a 150 foot span, fabric-covered wings, an enclosed cabin, and tricycle undercarriage. Much of the design – such as the bracing system – is quite original, but the details suggest that the drawing is in fact for a much smaller craft. The craft as specified would not have been strong enough, would not have met the weight criteria, and would have been under-powered. He was granted his patent, for 'certain improvements in locomotive apparatus and machinery for conveying letters, goods and passengers from place to place through the air,' but the proposal for the Aerial Transit Company had to go to Parliament, where it was greeted with derision.

Henson made a model of the plane in his patent; it weighed 14 pounds and had 40 square feet of wings. He tried to fly it in the Adelaide Gallery in London, but it was a complete

Replica of Stringfellow's steam-powered aircraft in the Chard mill where he achieved the first powered flight.

flop – literally. The press had a field day; the papers were full of mocking cartoons. There was, however, a more positive article in *The Times* of 30 March 1843, which concluded that '. . . possession of the long-coveted power of flight may now be safely anticipated'.

Henson and Stringfellow worked together on a new 20 foot model, but by 1845 Henson was losing his enthusiasm. Eventually he got married, emigrated to America, and patented a new safety razor. Stringfellow was left to carry on alone, and when the new model was finished he got workmen to carry it up to Bala Down for testing. He was so upset by people making fun of his work that he did this secretly, at night, and tried the first flight under cover of darkness. It was a disaster – the silk covering of the wings got wet with dew, and became so heavy that the machine could not fly. He tried again in the daytime – indeed he tried every day for seven weeks, but finally had to admit defeat.

And then, for the first time, he designed his own aircraft from scratch. Accounts are few, but we know that it had a 10 foot wingspan, with swallow-shaped wings, rather than Henson's rectangular design. The wing area was about 18 square feet, and its overall weight perhaps 9 lb including the super-lightweight steam engine.

Stringfellow flew his plane for the first time in the summer of 1848, inside the top floor of a lace mill, some 20 metres long. Outside he had had trouble with damp and with cross-winds. His aircraft had no fin, nor anything else to prevent it from veering left or right. So flying it inside, in still air, seemed a good plan. He launched it along a fixed wire, which ran down a slight slope for nearly half the length of the mill;

when the aircraft reached the end of the wire it released itself by a cunning catch. The wire launch enabled him to get a good smooth downhill run, so that by the time the machine started flying it was already moving at a reasonable speed, and was also flying exactly level, with no tendency to veer left or right. This last point was important, because the mill has a row of iron pillars down the middle, which means that the flight path was only about 20 feet wide; there was only 5 feet of clearance on either side.

In the first experiment, according to his son Fred, writing fifty years later, the tail was set at too high an angle, and the

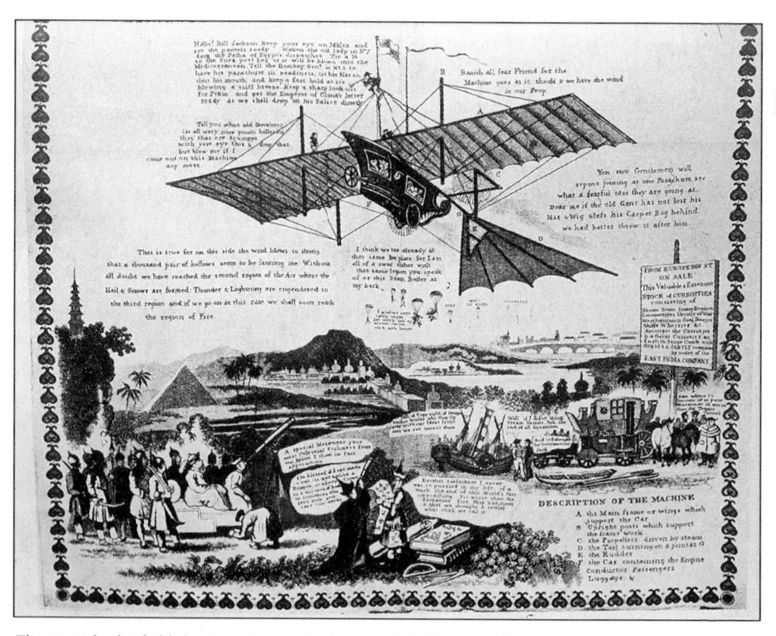

The press had a field day over Henson's dream of starting an airline.

machine rose too rapidly on leaving the wire. After going a few yards it stalled and slid back as if down an inclined plane; the point of the tail struck the ground and was broken. Once the tail was repaired it was set at a lower angle. The steam was again got up, the machine started down the wire and, upon reaching the point of self-detachment, gradually rose until it reached the farther end of the room, punching a hole in the canvas placed to stop it before it hit the wall.

This sketchy account is all we have, but several local worthies were there to witness this first powered flight, achieved by John Stringfellow in 1848.

Each town sign on the roads into Chard in Somerset shows a picture of Stringfellow's plane; there is a bronze replica in the High Street, and there are various important bits and pieces in Chard Museum.

George Boole and his Vision in a Field in Doncaster

Life today is full of computers; sometimes they seem to run our lives. But they might not run at all if it had not been for a vision experienced by a seventeen-year-old assistant teacher in a field in Doncaster.

George Boole was born in Lincoln on 4 November 1815. His father was a shoemaker, but probably spent too little time making shoes and too much messing about with scientific instruments and mathematical ideas. However, he did succeed in giving his son a lust for learning. Young George was a precocious schoolboy, and astonished the readers of his local newspaper by producing an elegant translation of some Greek verse – so elegant that another pedantic reader wrote to the editor and protested that such a young lad could not possibly have produced such a translation without a good deal of help. He probably hoped to go to university, but in 1831 his father's business failed, and so fifteen-year-old George had to go out to work in order to support the family.

Unable to find a job in Lincoln, he walked 40 miles north to Doncaster, and in July secured the post of usher, or assistant teacher, in Mr Heigham's School in South Parade. He did not enjoy being so far from home; it must have been at least two days' walk. He was lonely, and wrote home often, complaining that no one in Doncaster made gooseberry pies as good as his mother's. He was also rather unhappy at the school, a strict Wesleyan establishment where religion came first, and nothing else must be allowed to interfere. Some of the parents suspected George of reading mathematics books on Sundays, and even worse, he was accused of doing sums in chapel!

One problem was that he loved to read, but had no easy access to a library or other source of free books; so he had to buy his own. Because he didn't have much money, he always bought books that took a long time to read and therefore provided good value. He found the best of all were textbooks of mathematics, which took many hours to plod through. Later in life, he claimed that this was how he became seriously interested in mathematics. When he was neither teaching nor absorbing mathematics, he liked to go walking.

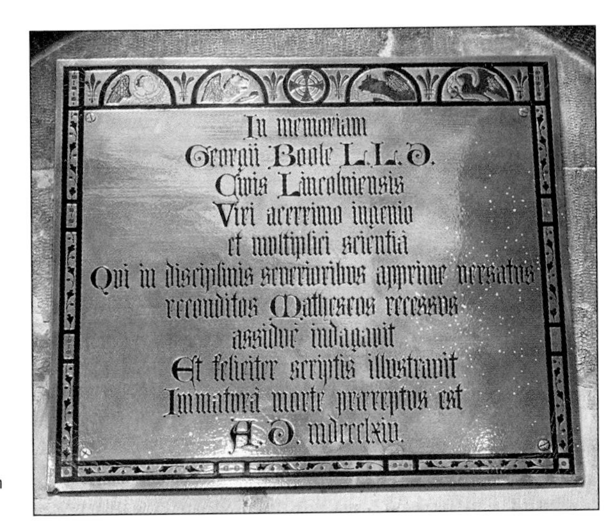

George Boole's memorial in Lincoln Cathedral.

He was lucky, for directly across the Great North Road he found Town Fields, a great expanse of common land, ideal for walking off the pain of a teenage exile. This was where he had his vision – a revelation that changed the world.

One cold day in January 1833 George was walking along thinking, when he was suddenly struck by an astonishing idea. He often talked about the moment later in life, and compared the experience with that of Saul on the road to Damascus. It changed his life, and it changed our lives too. George had learned from his reading that mathematics was highly successful in describing the working of the physical world; ever since Newton, scientists had been applying mathematics to all sorts of moving systems – from cannon balls to planets – and had found their motions could be described and predicted using simple mathematical laws.

George's idea was this: if mathematics could describe the physical world, could it also describe the mental world? If mathematical principles explained the functioning of cogwheels of machines, could they also explain the cogwheels of thought? Could he develop the maths to unravel the human mind?

At first this was only a flash of inspiration, and it took him fourteen years to work out the details, but eventually he wrote a long essay called *The mathematical analysis of logic, being an essay towards a calculus of deductive reasoning* (1847), and then a book called *An investigation into the laws of thought* (1854). These created tremendous interest. Bertrand Russell said: 'Pure mathematics was discovered by Boole, in a work which he called The Laws of Thought.' In his day he was regarded as the greatest logician since Aristotle.

Boole's memorial window, Lincoln Cathedral.

According to Boole's system, logical problems could be expressed as algebraic equations, and therefore solved by mechanical manipulation of symbols according to formal rules. There were only two values – 0 and 1, or False and True – and logical ideas could be added to one another: if (day =

Wednesday) and (time = afternoon) then the shops are shut. The shops remain open if either value is False.

Although Boole thought he had solved the mystery of the human mind, others were not convinced. Nevertheless, Boolean algebra was such an elegant system that it became widely known, admired and used. And in the 1930s, when Claude Shannon was trying to build the world's first computer at Massachusetts Institute of Technology, he found that it precisely described the behaviour of an array of electrical switches – each of which has just two positions, Off or On.

Shannon was working on the mathematics of information, and had reduced every choice to Yes or No. He represented these with a binary code, and called each unit of information a 'binary digit' or bit. So the fundamental ideas for electronic computers came straight from Boolean algebra.

George Boole was fired by Mr Heigham within a few weeks of his revelation, but he went back to Lincoln and started a school of his own. He married Mary Everest, niece of the surveyor of northern India, who gave his name to the world's highest mountain, and they produced a horde of successful children. He went on to become Professor of Mathematics at the University of Cork. Maybe he did not solve the mystery of the human mind, but the logic of every computer today is based on the idea that came to him in that flash of inspiration, in a field in Doncaster.

You can still go for an inspiring walk in Town Fields, Doncaster. Boole is commemorated by a window and brass plaque in Lincoln Cathedral and a plaque on the wall of 3 Pottergate, nearby.

Isambard Kingdom Brunel and his Atmospheric Railway

In 1844 there was railway mania. All over the country companies were being set up and permanent way laid down. The Stephensons and Locke had started in the north-west, while the Great Western Railway had been built with speed and enthusiasm by a young, thrusting, dynamic engineer; even his name was over the top: Isambard Kingdom Brunel.

Son of French engineer Marc Isambard Brunel and Sophia Kingdom, Isambard was born on 9 April 1806. As chief engineer for the Great Western Railway, he built Paddington station and Bristol Temple Meads, and invented Swindon. He designed the Clifton Suspension Bridge, the Tamar Bridge, and many others. He also built some of the first great iron ships – the *Great Western*, the *Great Britain*, and the gigantic *Great Eastern*, which in 1866 laid the first cable across the Atlantic.

For Isambard Kingdom Brunel, only the biggest and best was good enough. His projects were usually years late and hopelessly over budget, but he was the showman of the engineers. Even his top hat was vast, and he used to carry his plans in it. Once, when he was introduced to Queen Victoria, he bowed low, swept off his hat . . . and his plans cascaded across the ground.

The railway reached Bristol in 1841 and Exeter in 1844, and Brunel became engineer to the South Devon Railway, incorporated on 4 July 1844 with a capital of £1,100,000. He chose a flamboyant route down the west bank of the Exe, and along the seashore to Dawlish and Teignmouth, where

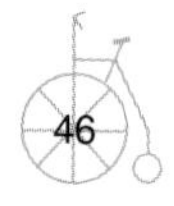

the trains still thunder along within yards of the sea. And he persuaded the directors of the SDR to approve the latest and most fashionable propulsion system. It had been tried out on a couple of test lines, but this was to be the first major railway designed from the start to be atmospheric.

The rails were normal, but on the sleepers between them was a cast-iron tube, 15 inches in diameter. A close-fitting piston ran along inside the tube, and was connected to the leading passenger car. The air was pumped out of the tube in front of the train, thus creating a vacuum; so the piston was pushed along by the pressure of the atmosphere behind it, and the piston pulled the train. It was indeed an atmospheric railway.

The piston was connected to the train by a rod which passed through a 3-inch wide slot along the top of the cast-

A section of cast-iron tube from the atmospheric railway. The arm connecting the train to the piston ran in the slot at the top of the tube, which was sealed by a leather flap in the flanges on either side.

iron tube. The slot was closed by a continuous flap of leather strengthened with iron framing and hinged along one edge, the other edge closing on the opposite side of the slot, the whole being made airtight with grease. The leather flap lifted to allow the rod to pass, and was then pressed shut again by a roller behind.

The vacuum was created by huge Boulton & Watt steam engines driving air pumps in pump-houses every three miles along the track. This created tremendous force. Suppose they pumped half the air out of the tube, and lowered the pressure inside to 8 lb/sq. in, then the force acting on the piston would have been more than half a ton – more than enough to move a lightweight train. On one epic test run outside Dublin, a young man called Frank Ebrington got into the front carriage, didn't realise the other carriages had not been coupled to it, and was hauled along a sharply curving track at a terrifying average speed of 84 mph. For the 1840s he was certainly the fastest man on Earth!

After many teething problems the South Devon atmospheric railway was opened to the public in September 1847. By January 1848 atmospheric trains were running all the way from Exeter to Newton Abbot. When the train reached a station they telegraphed ahead to the next pump-house and told them to switch on the pumps and make a vacuum ahead of the train. When all the passengers were aboard, the brakes were released and the train slid silently forward.

The passengers loved it. The trains ran quietly and smoothly, and without steam, smoke or smuts. What's more, they were often on time or even ahead. Speeds of 40 or 50 mph were normal, and one train ran from Newton Abbot to

Exeter in 20 minutes, which is faster than today's Intercity trains! Because the trains didn't need locomotives they were much lighter, and so had tremendous acceleration and deceleration. Also the rails could be lighter and cheaper.

The SDR atmospheric system cost £300,000 to install, and worked more or less satisfactorily for nine months, but then it ran into all sorts of problems. Casting the pipe was difficult; eventually it was done in Bristol by Tom Guppy, who managed to turn it out at the rate of a mile a week. Even more of a problem was the leather flap along the top. It had to be there to maintain the vacuum, but in the winter it sometimes froze solid and let in the air, while in the summer it dried out and cracked. In an effort to solve the problem and maintain the vacuum, greasers walked along the track smearing the leather flap with a mixture of lime soap and seal oil, or whale oil. Unfortunately the oil attracted rats, and the rats ate the leather – and that didn't do the vacuum any good either.

There were also pumping problems. When they switched on in the morning each pumping station was like the inside of a vacuum-cleaner bag; the first rush of air brought a mixture of oily water, rust, and dead rats and mice. The telegraph never worked, and the leather seal leaked; so the pumps had to run continuously to maintain the vacuum, and this was very expensive. There were other technical hitches. Atmospheric trains could not reverse; if they over-ran the platforms by a few yards, the passengers had to jump out and push the train back in. Shunting around stations was impossible. What is more, no one solved the problem of points – one track could not meet another, because there was no way of getting the rolling stock across the cast-iron tube between the rails.

However, what finally scuppered Brunel's atmospheric railway was a piece of financial sharp practice. In 1844 railway fever had been at its height, and Brunel had persuaded the Board to go atmospheric with a flurry of magnetic personality and the promise of cheaper running. By 1848 the tide had turned. The atmospheric system was out of fashion, and by a bit of dubious accounting the anti-atmospheric lobby managed to persuade the shareholders that the railway had made a loss in the first six months of the year. This was unheard of; no railway company had ever made a loss. In fact, they were owed a great deal of money for carrying mail, and the company was moving sharply into substantial profit, but the fudged accounts were enough; the atmospheric system was voted out. The last atmospheric train went up the line in the early hours of Sunday 10 September 1848, and the system closed down for ever.

When Isambard Kingdom Brunel worked himself to death at the age of fifty-three, his long-term friend and assistant Daniel Gooch wrote in his diary that he was a 'man with the greatest originality of thought and power of execution, bold in his plans but right. The commercial world thought him extravagant, but although he was so, great things are not done by those who sit and count the cost of every thought and act.'

The only remaining pumping station is next to the Courtenay Arms at Starcross, on the A379 5 miles south of Exeter; it now houses the Starcross Fishing and Cruising Club. A section of the cast-iron tube is displayed in the Museum of the Great Western Railway, Kemble Drive, Swindon SN2 2TA. Phone: 01793 466646: Fax: 01793 466615.

Joseph Paxton and the Crystal Palace

Although it sounds unlikely, giant lily leaves brought together the two best-known activities of Joseph Paxton, the extraordinary man who not only transformed the grounds at Chatsworth in Derbyshire, but also built the Crystal Palace for the Great Exhibition of 1851. Joseph Paxton was born in Bedfordshire on 3 August 1801, the son of a poor tenant farmer who died soon afterwards. When he left school, Joseph was sent to work on his brother's farm, where he was beaten and starved, but not paid. When he was seventeen he ran away to be a gardener.

He was determined to better himself, and always made the most of every position he got into. He had a succession of gardening jobs, and at Chiswick Gardens Arboretum became foreman but, because he earned only eighteen shillings a week, he had just decided to go to America to earn more, when one day he opened the door for the Duke of Devonshire, who owned Chiswick Gardens and lived next door. The duke took an instant liking to the lad, and although he was only twenty-three appointed him superintendent at his country home – Chatsworth House in Derbyshire. Wow! What a break!

On his first day at Chatsworth, Paxton was understandably nervous and keyed up. He arrived at 4.30 a.m., explored the grounds, climbed over the wall into the walled garden, set the men to work, watched the water-works in action, joined the housekeeper Mrs Gregory for breakfast, met her niece Sarah Brown and fell instantly in love – they eventually married

Joseph Paxton (1801–65).

and had a daughter – and all this before nine o'clock in the morning!

The Duke of Devonshire thought Paxton was wonderful, and more or less gave him a free hand with the gardens, so he set about building all sorts of magnificent display pieces. He made huge fountains, one of which spouts water up to 270 feet – twice the height of Nelson's Column. There is also a magnificent cascade of water down what is essentially a long flight of stone steps. The water for these displays came from a lake at the top of the hill behind the house. There are no pumps: gravity does all the work, and the high fountain can still be switched on just by turning a tap.

Paxton built an arboretum, a conservatory 300 feet long, and even a model village – Edensor. Apparently the duke was impressed by an architectural catalogue, and simply ordered one of each model! So every house is different. The duke adopted Paxton as a companion and confidant; they went everywhere together, and took one long trip around the Mediterranean.

In 1837 a traveller brought back from Guyana a fantastic new lily, but the experts at Kew Gardens were unable to get it to grow. Paxton got hold of a cutting, and designed a specially heated pool, using water-wheels to keep the water flowing. He managed to make the lily grow, and even he was staggered by its size. In three months it had eleven 5 foot leaves, and huge flowers. He named it *Victoria regina*, and gave Queen Victoria a bud. This lily was far too big to grow in most conservatories, and Paxton had to work out a way of designing bigger spaces. He wanted glass overhead, and he needed to dream up some simple structure that would hold up the glass. Inspired by the huge leaves of the lily, which were themselves a feat of engineering, he said, he tried floating his daughter Annie on a leaf and it worked.

So he designed a rigid structure made of radiating ribs connected by flexible cross-ribs. He tried it out, modified it, tried Mark 2, modified it again, and so on, until he got it to work. He used wood, because it was cheap and light, and he made the glass roof in ridges and furrows so that the maximum amount of light came in – even during the early morning and late evening light wasn't wasted by reflection. He designed special rafters that had gutters above the glass to collect rainwater and below the glass to collect condensation. For support he used hollow pillars that doubled as drainpipes. But the really brilliant idea behind the final design was that all the pieces were prefabricated, and simply bolted together on site. He designed the machines to make the parts, which were then manufactured in vast numbers.

In 1851 there was to be a Great Exhibition in Hyde Park in London. Clearly they needed a temporary building to house it, and a competition was held for the design of this structure. The judges included the great railway engineers George Stephenson and Isambard Kingdom Brunel, who rejected all

245 entries, and suggested their own plan, but this was so ugly it was turned down after a public outcry.

Joseph Paxton offered to put in a design, and was given two weeks. Within nine days he had on their desks a stunning version of his lily-leaf-supported greenhouse. It was simple to erect, it could easily be taken down again after the exhibition, and it was amazingly cheap – only £80,000 for a building big enough to hold twelve football pitches on the ground floor, and more than 100 feet high. Paxton raised the stakes by publishing his design in the *Illustrated London News*.

The building attracted great interest and disapproval in the press, and the magazine *Punch* sneeringly called it the Crystal

The Crystal Palace, built in Hyde Park to house the Great Exhibition of 1851.

Palace. Some authorities feared it would attract thieves and prostitutes, but the people loved it. In fact the whole thing was a phenomenal success, and Paxton was knighted, and became Sir Joseph Paxton.

There was a bit of a problem before it opened, because it was built with two huge elm trees inside, and a mass of sparrows came in out of the cold and nested in the elms, and made a lot of mess. How on earth could they get rid of the sparrows? Shooting was obviously impossible, with all that glass. The queen summoned the Duke of Wellington, and he, resourceful as ever, said, 'Well ma'am, you could try a sparrowhawk'. Biological control, in 1851!

The public lavatories in the Crystal Palace were installed by flamboyant plumber George Jennings, who decided to charge people a penny to go in. There was a storm of protest, but 827,280 visitors did indeed 'spend a penny' – which is probably where that expression came from! After the Great Exhibition, the Crystal Palace was taken down, piece by piece, and re-erected at Sydenham, where Paxton went to live. He became rich, famous, and Member of Parliament for Coventry, and died in 1865. The Crystal Palace was destroyed by a fire in 1936.

Chatsworth is open to the public and its magnificent grounds still owe much to Paxton's inventiveness; in particular the great fountain and the water cascade are strikingly attractive, and there is a camellia planted in 1851 and therefore perhaps by him, in one of his original arboretums. There's also an excellent and reasonably priced lunch to be had in the restaurant.

Sir George Cayley, Inventor of the Aeroplane

The world's first powered flight was achieved by John Stringfellow in 1848, but his aircraft was only a model. The first heavier-than-air flying machine to carry a person was built by another Yorkshireman, Sir George Cayley, and the epic flight took place in Brompton Vale in North Yorkshire in 1853.

In the little church in Brompton, poet William Wordsworth married his childhood sweetheart Mary Hutchinson on 4 October 1802. There is even a theory that his famous poem about daffodils was written not in the Lake District, as is generally supposed, but at Brompton, where there are also daffodils under the trees by a lake. William and Mary must have noticed that just behind the little church is a great house, called Brompton Hall, but they probably didn't realise that even while they were being married, the squire was busy in his garden shed designing the world's first aeroplane.

George Cayley was born on 27 December 1773. His family had lived at Brompton Hall for generations. When he was nineteen his father died, and George became the sixth baronet – Sir George Cayley. So he had both money and time, although he also had an estate to manage. He was always interested in scientific observation. At the age of fifteen he was timing the beats of a crow's wing, and while he was at school he measured the rate of growth of his thumbnail; it grew just half an inch in one hundred days.

For many years he enjoyed a close relationship with his intelligent cousin Miss Phil, but in 1795 he married a

difficult and brittle girl called Sarah Walker, the daughter of his tutor in Nottingham. Their relationship was generally uncomfortable, and he may well have come to build his aircraft because she made the atmosphere in the house so chilly, and his workshop provided a refuge.

By 1796 he was designing flying machines. From string, whalebone, and feathers he created little toy ornithopters that would fly when wound up. He went on to design toy gliders, modelling them roughly on the crow. He realised that flight involved two important factors – forward propulsion and lift – and that the two could be tackled separately. He came to the conclusion – as did Stringfellow and Henson forty years later – that birds could get lift without flapping. After all, many birds glide for long distances without a single flap, and without plummeting to the ground. Cayley set about investigating lift by using a whirling-arm machine.

Aerodynamic experiments are hard to control, because you have to organise a steady flow of air or wind speed, and he did this by the ingenious use of a whirling-arm. He made his experimental wing of about one square foot, which he reckoned was the area of a crow's wings, and fixed it to the end of a wooden arm three feet long, pivoted near the centre on a vertical rod, and nearly counterbalanced at the other end. He wound a string round the rod, passed the end over a pulley, and hung a weight from it. When he let go of the weight it would fall, pulling the rod round and making the arm whirl. By doing this indoors he could be sure the 'wing' was always moving at constant speed through the air.

According to legend, his wife would not have this apparatus in the house; so he waited his opportunity. Their first child, Anne, was due in 1796 and Sarah went to stay with her mother in Nottingham for her confinement. George immediately set up his whirling-arm apparatus on the top landing in the great staircase of the Hall, so that the weight had a clear 20 foot drop to the ground. He tried various angles for mounting the wing, and reckoned he got maximum lift at an angle of 6°. Then he built a glider, with the wings set at 6° up from the fuselage, and went out to test it in Brompton Vale, the field behind the house.

He was so delighted by how well it flew that he waxed lyrical about the flying machines of the future. He reckoned a glider would be the ideal way to get people down mountains: 'It was very pretty to see it sail down a steep hill, and it gave the idea that a larger instrument would be a better and safer conveyance down the Alps than even the sure-footed mule.'

He went on to design the best aerodynamic shape for slipping through the air, and planned an internal combustion engine to provide power. 'When we can get a hundred horse-power into a pint pot,' he wrote to *The Times*, 'man will be able to transport his family and possessions as readily by air as he now does by railway.' He asserted that flying was the future, and that we should all come to use 'that uninterrupted navigable ocean which comes to the threshold of every man's door. . . . We shall be able to transport ourselves and our families with their goods and chattels more securely by air than by water, and at a velocity of from 20 to 100 miles an hour.'

Unfortunately, for many years he was too busy to pursue flying. He invented rifling for the barrels of big guns. He suggested that passengers on trains should wear seat-belts. He designed a net like a cow-catcher to attach to the front of

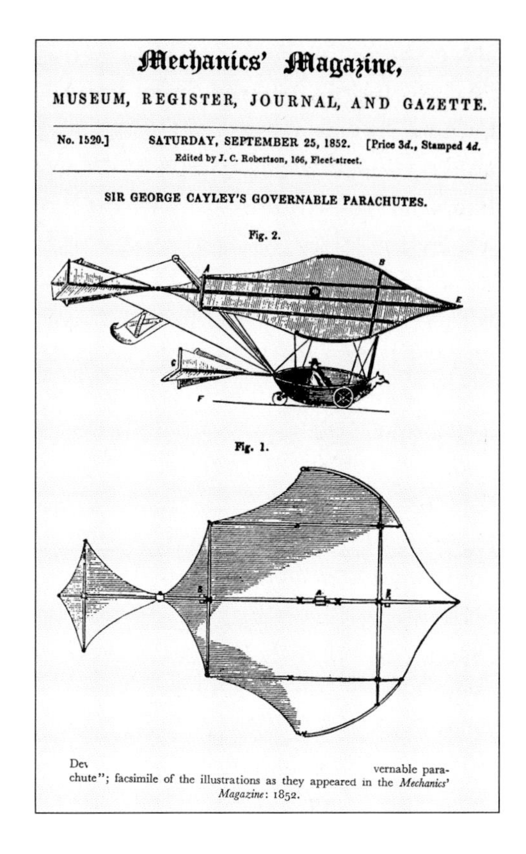

Mechanics' Magazine,

MUSEUM, REGISTER, JOURNAL, AND GAZETTE.

No. 1520.] SATURDAY, SEPTEMBER 25, 1852. [Price 3*d*., Stamped 4*d*.

Edited by J. C. Robertson, 166, Fleet-street.

SIR GEORGE CAYLEY'S GOVERNABLE PARACHUTES.

De\ vernable parachute"; facsimile of the illustrations as they appeared in the *Mechanics' Magazine*: 1852.

The New Flyer of 1852.

trains so that any workmen on the line would be scooped up rather than run over. He designed an 'Artificial hand for working men', and became MP for Scarborough. But in the 1840s he returned to aeronautics. He built a triplane which carried a boy off the ground on a downhill flight. And finally, in 1852, he built his New Flyer.

Cayley described his New Flyer in some detail in the *Mechanics* magazine of 15 September that year, although for some reason he gave the article the title 'Governable parachutes'. It was a monoplane with a kite-shaped wing and a tricycle undercarriage. In order to keep the weight down, Cayley had devised wheels with small rims and spokes of string in tension; in other words he had incidentally invented the bicycle wheel!

The following year, 1853, saw the first flight. Sir George was by now seventy-nine – rather old to be the world's first test-pilot – so he volunteered his coachman, probably one John Appleby, to take the tiller. The aircraft was launched from the grass field on the high east side of Brompton Vale by half a dozen farm hands running and pulling on ropes. It soared into the air, flew right across the valley – about 200 yards – and landed heavily on the grass the other side. The coachman clambered out of the wreckage, and said: 'Please, Sir George, I wish to give notice. I was hired to drive, not to fly!' Nevertheless, this was the world's first flight of a heavier-than-air person-carrying aircraft.

When the Wright brothers flew their aircraft *Flyer I* at Kittyhawk in North Carolina on 17 December 1903, they paid tribute to Cayley: 'About 100 years ago an Englishman, Sir George Cayley, carried the science of flying to a point which it had never reached before and which it scarcely reached again during the last century.'

In Brompton, 7 miles west of Scarborough, there's a pub called the Cayley Arms. Although Brompton Hall is now a school there is a plaque on the back of Cayley's workshop, visible from the road.

John Tyndall's Blue Sky

Although Tyndall's story is fairly extraordinary, he might have remained a competent but obscure physicist but for his charm and amazing ability to communicate scientific ideas to any audience. The impact he made on the public resulted in him getting to the very top of his profession, succeeding Michael Faraday at the Royal Institution – and working out why the sky is blue.

John Tyndall was born in Leighlinbridge, County Carlow, on 2 August 1820. Although the family owned a little land, they were quite poor and only the 'superior intellect' of John's father (also John) made sure that young John received a decent education at the nearby National School. He took an immediate interest in mathematics and obtained a job with the Ordnance Survey of Ireland, followed by a similar post in England. He ended up as a maths teacher at Queenswood College in Hampshire. It is here that Tyndall's character and scientific ambition really began to show themselves.

Having hauled himself up by his bootstraps to a fairly comfortable position, Tyndall realised that Queenswood College wasn't going to satisfy him intellectually. Together with a colleague, Edward Frankland, Tyndall travelled to Germany and enrolled himself at the great age of twenty-eight in the University of Marburg, where his tutor was Herr Bunsen, after whom the laboratory burner is named.

Although his first scientific paper was on the 'Phenomena of a Water Jet', Tyndall settled into some pretty obscure physics. He was particularly interested in the effects of pressure on crystals, which sounds rather dull but led him to work in Wales on how slate cleaves, and then to the Alps where the way glaciers move and crack puzzled physicists: how can apparently solid ice flow like a river? Perhaps the most dramatic outcome of this work was Tyndall's transformation into an accomplished Alpinist. He loved the mountains, and became one of the first men to scale the Matterhorn, and was the first to climb the Weisshorn in Switzerland. Yet none of this merited any public acclaim. All that was to change thanks to a brilliant lecture he gave in 1853.

Tyndall was invited to deliver one of the prestigious Friday lectures at the Royal Institution in London, where the great Michael Faraday was in charge. The lecture, whose title 'On the Influence of Material Aggregation upon the Manifestations of Force' is meaningless to most of us, was delivered on 11 February. It produced an extraordinary impression, and in May of the same year he was unanimously chosen as Professor of Natural Philosophy in the Royal Institution, working alongside Faraday.

This dramatic transformation seems to have resulted from Tyndall's brilliant performance in public. He was a great experimental scientist – but an outstanding demonstrator. He devised working experimental demonstrations of scientific ideas and techniques that immediately impressed and thrilled both scientists and the public. If he'd been alive today, he would no doubt have had his own television series!

Some of his demonstrations have become classics. To show the idea of resonance, he had a piano installed in the basement of the Royal Institution below the main lecture theatre. Upstairs he had a cello on a long pole, which passed through a hole in the floor and connected to the sounding board of the piano. When someone played the piano downstairs, the cello seemed magically to play itself, the strings resonating to the notes played on the piano. The hole in the floor is still there.

Another idea that interested him was 'total internal reflection', an optical phenomenon where light travelling through a piece of glass does not emerge into the air, but is instead reflected back into the glass. To show this, Tyndall invented the light pipe. All you need is a torch and a bucket with two holes. Seal one hole with a clear window, and fill the bucket with water, which will pour out of the remaining hole. Now shine your torch through the window and into the stream of water emerging on the opposite side of the bucket. It is well known that light travels in straight lines – yet it disappears! Instead, if you put your hand into the water, it is lit up by the light trapped in the stream by total internal reflection. Tyndall predicted that this phenomenon could be useful in telecommunication, and indeed that is exactly how fibre-optic cables use light to carry information round corners.

In 1867, when Faraday died, Tyndall took over as the Superintendent of the Royal Institution. Much of his work was to do with the way gases absorb radiation – it was Tyndall who showed that ozone absorbs ultraviolet light. As part of his investigation, he shone beams of light through filtered, very clean air. And he saw nothing. Normally you can see the beam, but no one had really stopped to wonder why. He now knew that the light beam you see from a spotlight or slide projector is in fact light scattered from tiny particles normally present in the air. And then came the bolt from the blue (almost literally). Since sunlight has to pass through air laden with these tiny particles, then surely a great deal of it must be scattered? So why can't we see the beam? Then he realised that we can see the light scattered from the sun. Different sized particles tend to scatter light from different parts of the spectrum – larger particles scatter more red, small ones more blue. If the dust in the atmosphere was mainly small, then it would scatter blue light and *that is why the sky is blue!*

Tyndall made his own blue sky to demonstrate this, of course, and you can do the same. By shining a beam of light from a slide projector through a tank of water, you can scatter more and more light by adding a little powdered milk. The tank takes on a distinctly blue appearance from the side, but when you look directly at the projector through the water and particles, it looks first yellow, then orange, then red, as you add milk powder. As the blue light is scattered from the sunlight, what is left looks yellow, which is why the sun is

The John Tyndall restaurant in Carlow.

yellow. Adding more milk produces a lovely red glow, just as at sunset you look at the sun through more atmosphere, with more particles in the way.

John Tyndall died after accidentally taking an overdose of chloral hydrate, but left a legacy of great science, and the idea that scientists have a responsibility to make their work interesting to the public.

Tyndall was a brilliant lecturer, and the Irish branch of the Institute of Physics organises a set of Tyndall lectures in schools every year.

Henry Bessemer's Anti-seasickness Boat

Seasickness can be a nightmare; many people start to feel queasy long before the mooring ropes are cast off, and spend even the smoothest Channel crossing retching miserably over the rail. One such person was Henry Bessemer, millionaire and steel king, and he decided to do something about it. He didn't just take pills; he designed and built the SS *Bessemer* as a permanent preventer of seasickness.

Henry Bessemer was born near Hitchin, Hertfordshire, on 19 January 1813. His father was a rich engineer, and Henry always enjoyed messing about with scientific and technical things. When he was seventeen, and in love, he made his first serious invention – embossed stamps to use on title deeds.

Henry Bessemer (1813–98).

People who needed a £5 stamp would usually peel one off an old deed, and thus avoid buying a new one. The government was losing £100,000 a year in revenue. His invention made this impossible, and he convinced the Stamp Office at Somerset House. They offered him the post of Superintendent of Stamps, at a salary of £700 a year – a small fortune in 1830! He was over the moon – now he could marry his beloved.

She then had an even better idea, which was simply to print a date on the stamps. When he told the Stamp Office, they said, 'Thanks very much, brilliant; we won't need you as Superintendent of Stamps now.' And he got nothing at all for his invention.

This made him furious; two brilliant ideas, but no money. After that, he found out about patenting. In all he took out 150 patents, covering a huge variety of ideas.

His first fortune came from making brass powder to use in 'gold' paint. His sister had made a portfolio of her paintings of flowers, and asked him to do the title on the outside. He thought this deserved better than just ink; so he bought some 'bronze powder' in two different colours, and paid 7*s* an ounce for it. He realised that if he could make this stuff cheaply he could make a fortune. So he invented machines to do it. The first one failed, but the second was a success.

Reckoning that a patent would not protect this process; he determined to keep it utterly secret. He had the full-size machines made in sections all over the country, and assembled them himself at his house in St Pancras, north London. He hired his three brothers-in-law to run the plant, and kept every room locked and the whole factory sealed against snoopers. Only five people ever went into the building, and they managed to keep the process secret for thirty-five years – much longer than a patent would have lasted.

But he really became an international jet-setter when he invented the artillery shell. The army were still using cannon balls, but Henry was sure that if they used a long thin projectile it would be not only heavier but also more accurate, because you could cut spiral grooves around it which would make it spin, and keep it on target. He built his own mortar, and made some experimental shells, which were highly successful. So he took out a patent in November 1854, and then tried to sell his idea to the War Department. They weren't interested; but a few months later he happened to have dinner with Napoleon in Paris. He sold the idea of shells to Napoleon, and had several trips to Paris on expenses. Unfortunately he found he was a terrible sailor; every time he crossed the English Channel he got horribly seasick.

Bessemer clearly hoped the stable saloon of the SS *Bessemer* would enable passengers to travel in unheard-of luxury; in fact the ship proved impossible to steer and demolished the pier at Calais.

The trouble with his new heavy shell was that the existing gun barrels weren't strong enough to take the extra pressure; so he decided to find a way of making better steel – which was how he came to invent the Bessemer Converter, which made him several million pounds.

Henry Bessemer was an astonishingly successful inventor and businessman; he was knighted in 1879. But I am relieved to say that even he did not always get it right. His most dramatic failure was the Bessemer Saloon Ship Company. He had suffered terribly from seasickness on his trips to France; so in December 1869 he began to spend time and a lot of money designing and making a cross-Channel boat in which no one could be seasick. He had two ideas. First, the boat was to be very long and thin, so that it would have minimal pitch – the ends of the boat would not go up and down much. Second, the entire cabin was mounted in gimbals with a great weight or even a gyroscope underneath it, so that however rough the sea was the cabin would always stay horizontal; while the hull of the boat would just roll and pitch about it.

The *Bessemer* was designed to prevent seasickness because the cabin stayed upright when the ship rolled.

He built a little model of his boat, but people remained unconvinced; so he constructed a full-sized mock-up of the cabin in a mobile hut mounted on a huge deck in a field near his house. He used a large steam engine to make the deck rock and roll, and then tried to keep the cabin horizontal. People still said it would never work, but he went ahead anyway, and spent more than £40,000 on floating the company and the boat.

Unfortunately, the huge heavy moving cabin made the boat so unstable that she was impossible to steer. On her maiden voyage on 8 May 1875, a beautiful calm day, the ship sailed from Dover, and in broad daylight comprehensively demolished the pier at Calais. The SS *Bessemer* never sailed again, and the company sank without trace!

Bessemer ran his steel works from Bessemer House, which still stands on Carlisle Street, Sheffield. The last Bessemer Converter to run stands outside Kelham Island Industrial Museum in Sheffield.

Sanitation and Statistics: the Story of Florence Nightingale

The idea that cleanliness is next to godliness may have encouraged some members of the church-going fraternity to wash, and medieval abbeys usually had lavatories – places to wash – but before about 1850 personal hygiene in Britain was rare. Elizabeth I astonished her courtiers by her enthusiasm for washing: she used to have a bath once a month, 'whether she needed it or not!'

Even though the Romans had organised extensive public baths in Bath and many other places, their example did not catch on. Until the middle of the nineteenth century there was

little piped water in Britain; rich people washed their faces in bowls of warm water brought in by the servants; poor people used a stream or the village pond if they were desperate.

Cities without proper sewers were revolting, and people complained bitterly about the smell. In the hot summer of 1858, when the banks of the Thames were covered for miles with decomposing sewage, the 'Great Stink' was debated in Parliament, where the curtains had to be drawn and soaked in chloride of lime to allow the members to breathe.

However, most people failed to realise that lack of sewers and proper sanitation was a major cause of disease. In the mid-1800s, infant mortality in English cities was 48 per cent; of all the babies born, only half lived to the age of five. They died from various illnesses – typhoid, cholera, diarrhoea – but basically they died because the sewage was not properly separated from the water supply.

The greatest advance ever made in human health was nothing to do with medicine, penicillin or surgery. It was the drive for simple sanitation, and it was brought about by such far-seeing doctors as William Budd and John Snow, and the remarkable Florence Nightingale, reluctant debutante and brilliant campaigner.

Dr Budd caught typhoid and recovered, so he took a deep interest when it struck in his village, North Tawton in Devon. By following its progress there and later in Bristol, he proved that it must be spread mainly in drinking water. John Snow came to the same conclusion about cholera in London's Soho, and took dramatic action – he removed the handle from the pump in Broad Street, where he knew the water was contaminated, and stopped the outbreak dead in its tracks.

Florence Nightingale's posh background made her an unlikely candidate for a heroine, but with her sharp insights, wide experience and missionary zeal, she revolutionised both the nursing profession and the management of hospitals. Her family travelled widely; she was born in Italy on 12 May 1820 in the city of Florence, and that's where she got her name. Her father was a wealthy bookish man, but her mother Frances cared only for society – where she was going to be seen, and with whom, what she was going to wear, which parties were beneath her station, and above all what were the marriage prospects for her two daughters.

Florence was supposed to behave like a lady, and occupy her time with flower-arranging and tapestry. She horrified her mother by going off and investigating hospitals, not just in England but even abroad, and she worked for three months at a hospital for the destitute – the Institute for Protestant Deaconesses at Kaiserwerth in Germany – where she was amazed to find many of the deaconesses were only peasants!

In 1854 the Crimean War broke out, and *The Times* sent out a reporter, William Howard Russell, who was in effect the first ever special war correspondent. He wrote back vivid reports about the bungling incompetence of the army commanders, and the horrors of the Crimea. In particular he wrote that although the French hospitals were well organised, the English wounded were terribly neglected. 'Are there no devoted women among us able and willing to go forth to minister to the sick and suffering soldiers?' he wrote.

Florence Nightingale answered the call. On 14 October she wrote to the Secretary of State for War, volunteering her services; on the same day he wrote to her, asking her to go.

Their letters crossed in the post. Just one week later she set off, with thirty-eight nurses. In the hospital at Scutari, they found appalling suffering. There were no bowls for water. No soap, no towels. No mugs, knives, spoons. No proper food. There were four miles of beds, and the soldiers lay in them with wounds, cholera, typhus, frostbite – all jumbled together. They died in their hundreds – mainly of disease. A thousand men died of disease before the first battle began. Florence would not let men die alone and uncomforted, so she sat beside their beds as they died; in the next couple of years she personally watched some two thousand soldiers die.

She applied basic common-sense ideas of sanitation and proper food, and in due course the death rate came tumbling down. In February 1855, just after she arrived, more than 50 per cent of the men admitted to hospital had died. By June, the figure was down to 5 per cent.

When she came back from the Crimea she was summoned to see Queen Victoria at Balmoral, and she began her task of

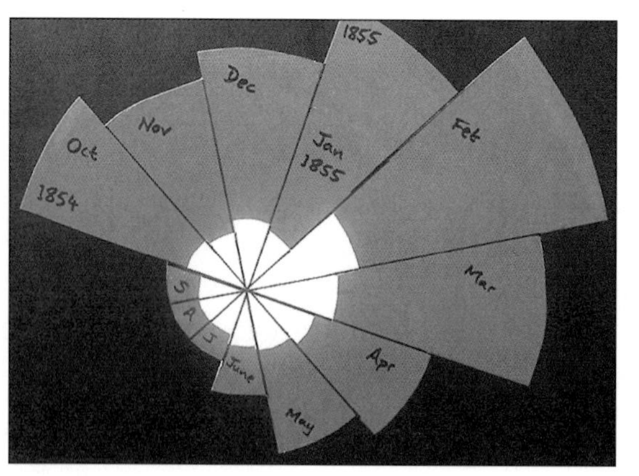

Florence Nightingale's 'coxcombs'. Each segment represents one month. The 'fans' show the numbers of soldiers who died in the Crimea: the white areas show the proportion who died from their wounds, the darker areas those who died of disease. Seven died from preventable disease for every one killed in battle.

persuading people that reform was necessary. Her main weapon, rather surprisingly, was statistics. Statistics had become all the rage.

Florence had collected statistics on everything in her hospital, from admissions, discharges, and causes of death, to the number of drains and the distance between the beds. She presented her results in striking graphics that she called 'coxcombs'. The whole thing represents a year. Each segment is a month. The areas represent the number of deaths. The inner light parts represent deaths from wounds and the outer dark parts represent deaths from preventable disease. For every soldier who died of wounds, seven died from preventable disease. In her report to the Royal Commission she wrote that every year the army took the fittest young men, and managed to kill 1,500 of them with poor food and disease. They might as well have been taken out on to Salisbury Plain and shot. These were ideas that people could understand.

Florence's modest face of the Nightingale family memorial at East Wellow.

Florence Nightingale achieved two remarkable things. Before she came along, nursing was regarded as a menial job of drudgery; most nurses were illiterate women of uncertain virtue who liked their drink and had no concept of hygiene. She raised the status of nursing to that of a caring profession.

She was hopelessly wrong in her theory of disease, but by a combination of common sense, drive, plain speaking and sheer hard work, she managed to get through to the authorities and bring about massive reform in hospital management.

Yet when she was dying she refused burial in Westminster Abbey, and insisted on being buried without any special fuss in the family grave in East Wellow, near Romsey. On the big family memorial, where the rest of the family have their names carved in full, one on each face, hers simply says F.N.

Perhaps she would like to be remembered as the caring nurse. Remember those four miles of beds at Scutari? If she could not get round them all during the day, she carried on alone through the night, with her Turkish oil lantern – the woman they loved – the Lady with the Lamp.

Florence is buried in the churchyard of St Margaret's Church at East Wellow, near Romsey. The Florence Nightingale Museum is in the corner of St Thomas's Hospital in London.

Henry Moule and the Earth-closet

In 1849 cholera struck Britain like a deadly tide, killing 55,000 people in a single year. Nowhere was worse hit than Dorchester, and in Fordington, just outside the ancient wall, the vicar worked tirelessly with the sick and the dying. On one day he held six funerals. They said Henry Moule stood between the living and the dead, boiling or burning contaminated clothes and bedclothes, and although he had not

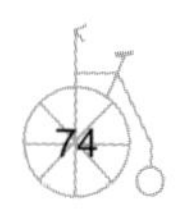

been popular, he gradually won the respect of the community. He also began to make the crucial connection between lack of sanitation and the spread of disease.

Moule described how, as he knelt beside a dying man, the overflow from the one privy shared by thirteen families trickled between his knees and the bed, and he saw the sewage bubbling up from the earth beneath the fireplace. Moule wrote to Prince Albert – the owner of the town – to explain the dreadful conditions; having written eight long letters without eliciting any sensible response, he set about his own methods of sanitary reform.

Henry Moule was born in Melksham on 27 January 1801, went to Cambridge, came to Fordington when he was twenty-eight, and stayed there for the rest of his life – more than fifty years. When he arrived with his wife Mary and two sons aged four and two, he found Fordington a sorry place. Thomas Hardy was to become a close friend of Moule's son Horace, and when he wrote *The Mayor of Casterbridge* Hardy used Mill Street, close by the vicarage, as the model for Mixen Lane – a slum of unmitigated horror, with gross overcrowding, appalling housing, poor sanitation and water; stinking ponds, crime, vice and prostitution.

Moule tackled his job with enthusiasm, making himself most unpopular with the parishioners by introducing a second fiery sermon in the Sunday service, and reforming the music until he drove the choir away. Moule even managed to get Dorchester races stopped. People jeered at his wife and children, and vandalised their lawn.

Undeterred, he ran the vicarage like a self-supporting commune, growing masses of vegetables, running a large hot-house, keeping cows, and earning some money by teaching not only his own eight children, but also seven paying boarders.

For some years he was chaplain to the troops in Dorchester Barracks, and he used the royalties from his 1845 book *Barrack Sermons* to build a church and a school at West Fordington. He was an enterprising man; he took out patents for the steam heating of greenhouses and for a new kind of fuel for steam engines. This scientific attitude led him to a fascinating discovery.

In the summer of 1859 he decided that his cesspool was intolerably disgusting, to him and the neighbours. So he filled it in, and instructed his household to use a bucket. At first he buried the sewage in a trench in the garden, but he discovered that in three or four weeks 'not a trace of this matter could be discovered': the sewage had decomposed. He suspected dry earth was the active agent, and to test his theory, put up a shed, sifted the dry earth beneath it, and mixed the contents of the bucket with this dry earth every morning. 'The whole operation does not take a boy more than a quarter of an hour,' he wrote, '*and within ten minutes after its completion neither the eye nor nose can perceive anything offensive.*'

So the dry earth deodorised the sewage and produced rapid decomposition. Moule's next step was to bring the earth into the house, dry it in a metal box under the kitchen range, and mix it in the bucket after every use . . . And in due course he developed a brand-new earth-closet – a sort of commode, with a bucket underneath the seat. Behind the seat was a hopper which he filled with dry earth. When he had finished using the closet, he pulled a handle, and a measured amount of dry earth was delivered into the bucket, to cover the offering.

He found he could recycle the earth, using the same batch several times, and he began to grow lyrical with rage at water-closets and praise for the earth: 'Water is only a vehicle for removing it out of sight and off the premises. It neither absorbs nor effectively deodorises. The great agent is dried earth, both for absorption and for deodorising offensive matters.'

And, he said, he no longer threw away valuable manure, but got a 'luxuriant growth of vegetables in my garden'. He backed up this last point with a scientific experiment, persuading a farmer to fertilise one half of a field with earth used five times in his closet, and the other half of it with an equal weight of superphosphate. Swedes were planted in both halves, and those nurtured with earth manure grew one third bigger than those given only superphosphate. Moule quoted a biblical precedent for his efforts, from a set of

Henry Moule, champion of the earth-closet, with his family and household at the vicarage where he did much of his research.

instructions about cleanliness in Deuteronomy, chapter 23 verse 13: 'With your equipment you will have a trowel, and when you squat outside, you shall scrape a hole with it and then turn and cover your excrement.'

Many people think the earth-closet is a bit of a joke, but Moule was convinced that it was the future. He worked out the implications; if used by a family of six, the earth-closet would need 50 kg of earth per week; so a town of 10,000 would need 17 tons of earth a day – but only borrowed!

He took out a patent in 1860, and set up the Moule Patent Earth-Closet Company Ltd, which manufactured and sold a wide variety of earth-closets, the expensive models made of mahogany and oak. They were even manufactured abroad under licence – in Hartford, Connecticut, for example, by the Hartford Earth-Closet Company.

Moule wrote a string of tracts and pamphlets, including *The advantages of the dry earth system, and Manure for the million – a letter to the cottage gardeners of England*. He also tried hard to get government support, with an 1872 paper on *Town refuse – the remedy for local taxation*. His main point was that to provide mains water and sewers was fantastically expensive, and the sewage still had to decompose somewhere. If everyone looked after their own there would be enormous saving in taxation, and much less spread of disease.

He managed to convince a lot of people: 148 of his dry-earth closets were used by two thousand men at the Volunteer encampment at Wimbledon in 1868; 776 were used in Wakefield Prison. The combination of economy and health was powerful. In 1865 the Dorset County School at Dorchester changed from water-closets to earth-closets, eliminated smells and diarrhoea, and cut the annual maintenance costs from £3 to 50p! Lancaster Grammar School also brought in earth-closets, but for less scientific reasons: the WCs were always out of order 'by reason of marbles, Latin grammar covers, and other properties being thrown down them'.

For some decades in the second half of the nineteenth century the earth-closet and the water-closet were in hot competition. Almost everything Moule said was true, and much the same arguments are used today by the champions of bioloos and composting lavatories. Unfortunately, flushing does rapidly remove the sewage from the house, and as a result – in rich countries – the water-closet is winning, for the moment. . . .

Henry and Mary Moule lie in the top corner of the graveyard below the church in High Street, Fordington, right outside Dorchester. Moule Close is beside the church. There is an original Moule earth-closet in Dorset County Museum; 01305 262735.

Colin Pullinger and his Perpetual Mousetrap

Mice have always plagued people; ever since the first cave-dwellers began to store food in a larder, mice have been there to make the most of it. Whenever people move into any sort of home, mice move in right alongside; for thousands of years people must have been inventing ways to get rid of

them. So the mousetrap has become a sort of symbol of human ingenuity.

The earliest mousetraps were probably just holes in the ground; the advanced versions were bottles sunk into the ground, so that the mice could not climb out up the slippery walls. Among the earliest known mechanical traps was the pit-fall trap, which was essentially a hole in the ground with a trapdoor, traditionally baited with a mixture of oatmeal and honey. The mouse came along, smelled the bait, stepped on the trapdoor, and dropped into the pit – or probably into a bucket of water.

Today the traditional bait is cheese; indeed poor-quality or plain cheap Cheddar cheeses are sometimes called 'mousetrap'. Most modern traps have metal springs; when the mouse touches the bait it releases a catch and a stiff wire loop snaps viciously down on the mouse's neck, usually killing it instantly. These traps are neat and powerful, but they have two disadvantages. First they are considered by some to be inhumane; occasionally the mouse is not killed, but injured and left in pain. Secondly, the trap can catch only one mouse at a time. Once it's sprung it's sprung, and other mice can come along and eat the cheese with impunity.

Pullinger's perpetual mousetrap. He claimed that in a single trap he caught twenty-eight mice in one night.

Both of these drawbacks were solved by Hampshire man, Colin Pullinger, born in 1814 in Ivy Cottage in Selsey. Despite the many

COLIN PULLINGER,
SELSEY, NEAR CHICHESTER,
Contractor, Inventor, Fisherman, and Mechanic,

FOLLOWING THE VARIOUS TRADES OF A
BUILDER, CARPENTER, JOINER, SAWYER, UNDERTAKER
Tanner, Cooper, Painter, Glazier, Wooden Pump Maker,
PAPER HANGER, BELL HANGER, SIGN PAINTER,
BOAT BUILDER,
CLOCK CLEANER, REPAIRER OF LOCKS, AND KEYS FITTED,
Repairer of Umbrellas and Parasols, Mender of China and Glass,
Copying Clerk, Letter Writer, Accountant, Teacher of Navigation,
GROCER, BAKER, FARMER,
Assessor and Collector of Taxes, Surveyor, House Agent, Engineer, Land Measurer, Assistant Overseer, Clerk at the Parish Vestry Meetings, Clerk to the Selsey Police, Clerk to the Selsey Sparrow Club,
Has served at Sea in the four Quarters of the World, as Seaman, Cook, Steward, Mate and Navigator.

THE MAKER AND INVENTOR OF THE FOLLOWING:
AN IMPROVED HORSE HOE, AN IMPROVED SCARIFIER,
A newly-invented Couch Grass Rake, a Machine to Tar Ropes, Model of a Vessel to cut asunder Chains put across the Mouth of a Harbour,
A CURIOUS MOUSE TRAP,
Made on a scientific principle, where each one caught resets the trap to catch its next neighbour, requires no fresh baiting, and will catch them by dozens,
A Rat Trap on a peculiar Construction,
That will catch and put them into the Trap,
An improved Mole Trap, an improved Velocipede, Model of a fast-sailing Yacht on an improved construction, 2ft long, and challenged to sail against any boat of the same length in the world, &c, &c, &c.

CRABS, LOBSTERS, AND PRAWNS SENT TO ANY PART OF ENGLAND,
MOUSE TRAPS LET ON HIRE.

Pullinger's trade card.

exotic professions claimed on his trade card, he ended up as a carpenter, inheriting the family business, and then, in about 1860, he invented a new mousetrap. This was a 'perpetual mousetrap' – one that would catch mouse after mouse – and the mice were not killed or even injured.

The trap had a hole in the middle of the top, for the mice to go in, attracted by the smell of the bait kept in a perforated bait-box inside. Below the entrance hole was the critical mechanism, a cruciform beam like a see-saw which the mouse would tip with its weight. Once it had tipped, the mouse could no longer reach the entrance; so its only way out of the compartment was through a one-way door into the end of the box. Once it had gone through this door, there was no escape, and the trap was set for the next mouse, which would find its way to the other end of the box. Colin always stressed how humane it was; the mice were unharmed, and could presumably be set free in your neighbour's garden!

This mousetrap was very successful, both operationally and financially. His advertising claimed that he had caught twenty-eight mice in one trap in a single night, and that in nine months a farmer had caught nearly 1,000 mice in one trap.

The factory grew until Pullinger employed forty men and boys; he was the biggest employer in Selsey. They had horse-powered circular saws and drills; they could make a trap in four and a half minutes, and they made 960 a week. By 1885 they had sold two million, at half a crown apiece, and mousetraps went on being made in Selsey until 1920.

The success of his enterprise lends support to the aphorism coined by the American writer Ralph Waldo Emerson: 'If a man write a better book, preach a better sermon, or make a better mousetrap than his neighbour, tho' he build his house in the woods, the world will make a beaten path to his door.'

Pullinger's house, Ivy Cottage, still stands in Selsey, but there is no obvious trace of the yard where he made his mousetraps.

Robert Fitzroy, Inventor of the Weather Forecast

Most of us take weather forecasts for granted. They appear daily in the papers, hourly on the news, and on TV even have their own show. For most of us, predictions of tomorrow's weather are of academic importance, but for farmers, pilots and fishermen, knowing the weather in advance is crucial. The first person to attempt systematic weather forecasting was Robert Fitzroy, a naval man, a brave and gallant sea-captain and a brilliant sailor. As Charles Darwin discovered, he was a difficult man to live with, and he came to a tragic end.

Robert Fitzroy was born at Ampton Hall, a few miles north of Bury St Edmunds in Suffolk, on 5 July 1805 – three months before the Battle of Trafalgar. He was the second son of the second son of the 3rd Duke of Grafton, and his mother died when he was five years old, so he probably had rather a tough and disciplinarian childhood. He went to naval college, and then to sea, and when he was only twenty-three the captain of his survey ship died, and Fitzroy was appointed to take command. The ship was the *Beagle*.

For her second voyage to South America in 1831 he decided to take along a companion – some well-bred gentleman to share his day-cabin and to dine with. After much thought, he decided the right sort of person would be a scientist, who should bring on board culture and interesting conversation.

The *Beagle* was only 90 by 24 feet, but carried a total crew of seventy-four, including a carpenter, a blacksmith, and a missionary. After a curious selection process Fitzroy offered the post of ship's naturalist to a young man called Charles Darwin, who jumped at the chance, even though his father objected at first, and the cabin was so small he could not stand upright in it. Neither of them knew the voyage would last five years, nor that Darwin would as a result of it write his wildly controversial book *On the Origin of Species*.

Fitzroy was neurotic and irascible, and sharing a cabin with him for five years must have been a considerable ordeal. Nevertheless, the voyage was a major success. When they returned, Fitzroy wrote an account of the journey in two volumes; Darwin wrote a third volume which came to be called *The Voyage of the Beagle*.

In 1843 Fitzroy became Governor of New Zealand, but left under a cloud a couple of years later, and returned to England. His difficult character stood in the way of his

Five years on the *Beagle* with the difficult Robert Fitzroy must have been a challenge for Charles Darwin.

landing a senior naval or diplomatic post, which is probably why in 1854 he took up the curious position of Head of the Meteorological Department of the Board of Trade. He was determined to make a success of the job, and a name for himself, and in 1861 he invented the weather forecast.

First he asked ships' captains, once they reached port, to post him details of the weather they had encountered. Then he saw the potential of the new electric telegraph, which would allow him to gather information much more rapidly and reliably. In order to ensure it was accurate and consistent, he set up twenty-four observing stations around the country, and issued each with a standard barometer and instructions on how to use it. Each day he compiled a summary in the form of a synoptic chart or weather map.

Every year in the early 1850s about a thousand ships were wrecked and some thousand lives lost near the British coast. At three in the morning on 26 October 1859 the sailing ship *Royal Charter* sank in a gale off Anglesey, with the loss of 400 lives and half a million pounds' worth of gold bullion. Fitzroy wrote a report about the disaster, and pointed out in words of one syllable that the storm could have been predicted at least twelve hours in advance using the information he had gathered. If the captain had been warned, he could have avoided the storm and saved the ship.

Fitzroy started to issue storm warnings; he invented a simple display system. A solid black cone point downwards – a 'south cone' – warned that a southerly gale was imminent; a 'north cone' – point up – warned of a northerly gale. These cones were used in every port, and provided useful warnings to sailors for more than a hundred years.

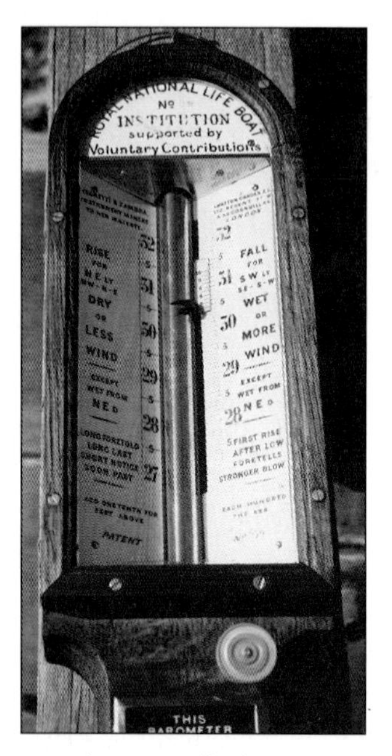

Fitzroy barometers, like this one from Sheringham, were provided to help fishermen predict the weather.

Encouraged by the success of his storm warnings, Fitzroy went further, and in August 1861 began to predict the weather. People knew a good deal about weather – for example, Cristoph Buys Ballot's Law said that if you stand with your back to the wind in the northern hemisphere then atmospheric pressure is lower on your left than on your right; and many 'experts' were happy to predict what they thought would happen locally the next day, but no one before Fitzroy had seriously tried to forecast the weather for the whole country. From 1862 his weather forecasts were printed in *The Times*, and aroused considerable interest. The British have always been fascinated by weather, and when people saw published forecasts they were amazed and delighted – except that the forecasts were often wrong. Today we are used to inaccurate weather forecasting. We know that even with the help of vast computers the meteorologists cannot be perfect, since the great engine of the atmosphere is too complex to be described by the models the forecasters use. Mathematical chaos ensures that the minutiae of meteorology will always be unpredictable.

However, in Fitzroy's day, people did not understand this, and he became the butt of terrible complaints and jokes. In

1864 questions about his forecasts were asked in the House of Commons. Even *The Times* said 'we must . . . demand to be held free of any responsibility for the too-common failures which attend these prognostications. During the last week Nature seems to have taken special pleasure in confounding the conjectures of science.'

As a fundamentalist Christian, Fitzroy had been seriously offended when Darwin's *Origin of Species* was published in 1859, since it seemed to suggest that God had not designed all creatures great and small – and it was all because he had taken Darwin on the *Beagle*. Now the most important people in the country, far from being impressed by his skill and ingenuity in predicting the weather, were pouring scorn on his incompetence. On 30 April 1865, Admiral Robert Fitzroy took his razor, cut his own throat, and died.

Fitzroy barometers are still preserved in a few maritime museums around the country.

William Banting's Diet

William Banting, born in 1797, was a short, fat undertaker and furnisher of funerals in St James's Street, London. As he grew older he became more corpulent; he was only 5 feet 5 inches tall, but by the time he was sixty-five he weighed 14 stone 6 pounds (92 kg), and could no longer tie his shoe-laces. He had to go downstairs backwards, and slowly, to avoid excessive strain on the ankle joints, and with every exertion he 'puffed and blowed' in a most unseemly way. This was most distressing for him, since his job as a smart undertaker required decorous behaviour and respectful quietness.

He consulted several doctors, and asked how he could reduce his size. They told him to take plenty of exercise, so he walked long distances, and then tried rowing. He actually rowed a boat for two hours before breakfast every day. But the result was that he grew hungrier and hungrier – and heavier and heavier.

He visited fifty Turkish baths in a vain attempt to sweat off his pounds. He drank gallons of patent slimming medicines. He visited spas to take the waters. He even – in desperation –

BANTING'S DIET

Breakfast	4–6 oz beef, mutton, kidneys, broiled fish, bacon, or any cold meat except pork 1–2 oz dry toast	1 large cup black tea
Dinner	10–12 oz of any fish except salmon, any meat except pork any vegetable except potato 2 oz dry toast fruit out of a pudding any kind of poultry or game	2 or 3 glasses of good claret, sherry, or Madeira but NO champagne, port, or beer
Tea	4–6 oz fruit a rusk or two	1 large cup black tea
Supper	6–8 oz meat or fish, as dinner	1 or 2 glasses claret
Nightcap		1 tumbler gin, whisky, or brandy

tried the new-fangled practice of sea-bathing. None of these things did any good. Then, because he was going deaf, he went to Soho Square and consulted Mr William Harvey. Mr Harvey said his deafness was caused by corpulence, and that the remedy was to go on a diet. He told Banting not to eat bread, butter, milk, sugar, beer, soup, potatoes or beans, but to eat mainly lean meat, fish and dry toast.

This is basically a high-protein, low-carbohydrate diet, although it seems to have been pretty generous with alcohol. Indeed the quantities of everything seem substantial, with three square meals a day, topped off by a nightcap of a tumbler of gin, whisky or brandy – although without any added sugar! In spite of the enormous intake of alcohol, the diet was successful. Within a year, Mr Banting lost more than 3 stone, and he felt better than he had for twenty years. He was so delighted at having lost so much weight by such simple means that in 1863 he wrote a pamphlet called 'A Letter on Corpulence, addressed to the Public'.

This, too, was an immense success. Tens of thousands of copies were bought by others who wished to be slimmer. The word 'Banting' became synonymous with dieting; and 'to bant' became a household phrase – 'I say, you do look well! Are you banting, my dear?' As a result of this, William Banting became quite rich and enormously famous, and thousands of people followed his advice – which seems rather unfair, really, since the advice came in the first place from Mr William Harvey of Soho Square.

So many copies of his pamphlet were sold that many must still exist, but they are hard to find.

Eugenius Birch, Genius of the Pier

Ozone these days has rather negative connotations – we either hear about the hole in the ozone layer caused by nasty stuff from leaking fridges and spray cans, or about ozone as a poisonous gas produced by older photocopiers and other electrical devices. Ozone is good for the planet, but bad for people. But in the mid-nineteenth century things were very different, and ozone was considered to have such health-giving properties that people travelled to the seaside, where there was lots of ozone, in order to consume as much as possible. They took all this rather literally, and it was thought you got maximum benefit if you could somehow actually walk over the water. Since even Victorians couldn't do this unaided, they invented the pier.

The first piers were 'chain piers', essentially suspension bridges going nowhere. They were made with wooden piles

Birch's West Pier at Brighton open to the elements for maximum ozone exposure.

The West Pier at Brighton today. Although damaged by ships and allowed to fall into decline, Birch's structure has survived.

driven into the seabed, four iron towers put on these to hold the chains, and the wooden deck suspended from the chains. Since the four towers and two chains carried the entire load, there was a limit to the weight of construction and of people the pier could support, and they were not very big. The chain pier at Brighton, one of the first in Britain, had a wooden deck only 13 feet wide. It really couldn't cope with the demand, and the wooden piles tended to get eaten away. The man who solved the problem of the pier was Eugenius Birch.

Although famous for his piers, Eugenius was really a railway man. Born at Shoreditch, London in 1818, like many boys of the age he was fascinated by the engineering of the time, and spent much of his spare time doing engineering drawings. Unlike most boys, he had one of his designs accepted. He had sent a model railway carriage to the

London and Greenwich Railway Company, and they liked the way he fitted his wheels. Apparently he had them under the carriage, where the design they had been using had wheels sticking out to the side. The Birch design would have given more space in the carriage, and they took it up. He was clearly artistic, and there is evidence of his having received many prizes for his drawings.

With his brother John he set up an engineering partnership, and together they built many miles of railway in Britain, and was even involved in the Calcutta–Delhi line in India. But it was in 1853 that he finally met his pier of destiny. The scene was Margate, and he had been commissioned to build the town's pier. Eugenius and John already had a revolutionary technology in place. The previous year they had patented a new method for boring holes for drainpipes, using screw threads on the end of long poles to drill holes horizontally into the ground. Could the idea be turned around and used for piers? They invented the screw pile.

A wrought-iron screw bit was welded on to the end of a cast-iron column. The whole thing was rotated so that the column drilled itself into the seabed. Wrought iron was used for the screw because it was not so brittle as cast iron and could stand being drilled into chalk or gravel. The cast-iron column was to be left in place, and the pier was to stand on a forest of these. Birch found that cast iron was quite resistant to corrosion by the sea, and indeed many of his columns survive today. The net result of the new technology was a new design. Instead of having just four load-bearing wooden piles, he could have as many cast-iron ones as he liked. They were driven into the ground by manual labour at first, then by machine in later projects, and linked together with cross-braces and struts. The pier decking was mounted on top.

The Margate pier was a huge success, and other commissions followed. The greatest was for a new pier at Brighton – what is now the West Pier. On Saturday 6 October 1866 after two and a half years of screw piling, the pier was opened. It was 1,115 feet long and 140 wide at the pier head. Initially it was completely open to the elements except for six small ornamental houses. At its narrowest it was 55 feet – four times as wide as the old chain pier.

Tourists were each charged a shilling to experience the spectacle. Dignitaries gave speeches; one described the new pier as 'a kind of butterfly upon the ocean to carry visitors upon its wings and waft them amongst the zephyrs and balmy breezes of Brighton'. The band of the 68th Light Infantry Regiment provided stirring music for the crowds. The Royal Standard was hoisted and the gun detachment of the Coastguard sounded a 21-gun salute from the centre of the pier. The illuminations were switched on later, followed by a grand display of fireworks.

Over the years, the pier evolved. Pavilions and wind screens were added as it was transformed from a promenading pier into an entertainment pier, featuring such bizarre acts as Captain Camp, the one-legged swimmer, Miss Louise Webb and her unique, scientific and graceful underwater performance and even flea circuses. Birch went on to build fourteen piers all over Britain, including at Aberystwyth, Hastings, Blackpool and Bournemouth.

Curiously, although we think of the demise of the pier as a relatively modern phenomenon, the peak season for the

Brighton West Pier was just after the First World War, with over 2 million visitors. This was down to 900,000 in 1930 and signalled another change in the pier, from entertainment venue to funfair.

Today the pier is in a sorry state and in 2001 is only open to the public once daily at 1400 hours, at their own risk. This is possible only because the iron screw piles are still standing over 130 years after they were put in place, a tribute to the genius of Eugenius Birch.

The Long Drop of William Marwood

Before 1875 a prisoner sentenced to death was hanged by being suspended on a rope and allowed to die slowly by strangulation. This barbaric procedure was changed by William Marwood, who worked out how to break the victim's neck, causing instant death.

William Marwood (public hangman 1872–83).

Marwood was a Lincolnshire cobbler, with premises at 6 Church Street, Horncastle. Over several years he repeatedly applied for permission to act as hangman, and was finally given his first commission in 1875, when on 21 December he hanged Henry Wainwright in Lincoln gaol.

WM. MARWOOD,
EXECUTIONER,
CHURCH LANE,
HORNCASTLE,
LINCOLNSHIRE, ENGLAND.

Marwood's business card.

Marwood did not hide this part-time profession. He used to go to fairs and show off his ropes for sixpence a time. He put up a big sign above his shop, and he charged high prices for his bootlaces; people came from miles around and bought them because they were the hangman's laces. He became famous, and was frequently mentioned in music-hall songs and jokes, such as 'If pa killed ma, who'd kill pa?' Answer: 'Marwood.'

Before Marwood, death was slow and painful: the pressure of the rope crushed the windpipe, cutting off the supply of air to the lungs. A typical victim lost consciousness after three or four agonising minutes, and died after about ten. Marwood's idea was to use a long rope and a trap-door high up on a scaffold, so that when the trap was opened, the victim fell 7 or 8 feet before reaching the end of the rope. Marwood tied the rope snugly tight, with the knot at the point of the jaw under the victim's left ear. This ensured that when the rope tautened it snapped the head back, causing a fracture dislocation of the atlanto-axial junction. The top vertebra, the 'atlas', sits on the second one, the 'axis'. A peg of bone sticks up from the axis into a socket in the atlas, and allows the head to swivel. Put your fingers to the back of your neck, and you can feel the atlas turn with your head, while the axis below does not move. When the head is snapped back by the long drop, the peg breaks, the neck kinks rapidly, the spinal cord is crushed, and the resulting spinal shock causes instant loss of consciousness, even before the heart stops beating. Because it caused immediate brain death, Marwood's long drop was more humane that the previous method; he used to say of his predecessors, 'They hanged 'em; I execute 'em.'

Marwood's shop is marked by a plaque at 6 Church Lane, Horncastle, Lincolnshire; it is now part of the house next door. Pictures of Marwood and his card are from the Local Studies Library, Lincoln Central Library, by courtesy of Lincolnshire County Council, Education and Cultural Services Directorate.

And the Earth Moved: John 'Earthquake' Milne

In 1974 the Japanese ambassador to Great Britain made a pilgrimage to a tiny, rather nondescript village on the Isle of Wight. On a grassy bank he planted a cherry tree in memory of a local resident. This man, better known in Japan than in Britain, made the village of Shide the world centre for seismology. He was known as John 'Earthquake' Milne.

John Milne was born in Liverpool in 1850. At thirteen, he won a trip to the Lake District, and was so struck by the beautiful hills that he ran away to Ireland to see the scenery there. However, he soon buckled down to a career in geology, studying at the Royal School of Mines. He clearly had a taste for adventure, and despite his parents' misgivings undertook a dangerous expedition to Iceland in 1871. Having caught the exploration bug, he went to Newfoundland and Arabia, before his career really took off.

In 1875 Milne was offered the post of Professor of Geology and Mining at the Imperial College of Engineering, Tokyo. This was good news and bad: despite his adventurous streak, Milne got terribly seasick, and had to travel to Tokyo overland, through a Siberian winter. In 1875 there wasn't a railway, and he had to travel by carriage, boat, sleigh and even camel. On the night he arrived, there was an earthquake, and although his first job was to catalogue Japanese volcanoes, earthquakes really fascinated him.

Milne had two great achievements. First, he founded the scientific study of earthquakes (he is known as the 'father of modern seismology'). Secondly, he invented the instrument that made it possible, the horizontal pendulum seismograph. Milne's primary aim was to record how the earth moves in earthquakes. There were two rather obvious problems. You didn't know when, or where, the earthquake would occur. The first problem could be easily but tediously solved by recording earth movements all the time, just in case an earthquake happens. The second had proved insoluble: unless you are lucky enough to be near the epicentre of the earthquake, there are no discernible earth movements. Milne realised that in fact an earthquake would cause a disturbance at a distance, possibly all round the world, but that in most places the earthquake waves would be drowned by local effects, such as people walking about

John 'Earthquake' Milne (1850–1913).

in the next room. However, he had defined the problem. It would be possible to detect earthquakes at a distance if there was something characteristic about earthquake waves that let you separate them from the bigger local disturbances.

Although the Chinese had used seismoscopes as long ago as AD 132, the first real seismometer was made by J.D. Forbes at Comrie in Perthshire in 1841, using an inverted pendulum. Milne also used a pendulum, but realised that earthquake waves would show up as sideways movements, so his was a horizontal pendulum. Essentially a pivoted arm with a weight on the end, suspended by a wire, he found that he could tune the seismometer by adjusting the length of pendulum arm, the size of weight and the tension in the wire. This brilliant device was able to pick up the characteristic earthquake waves, even when there were much bigger local vibrations. He made it into a seismograph, capable of continuously recording earthquakes, by attaching a pen to the end of the arm. Milne is a hero in Japan both because he put the study of earthquakes on a scientific footing, and because his understanding of earthquake waves allowed him to make the first serious suggestions about how earthquake damage to buildings could be prevented.

On 17 February 1895 Milne's house and observatory in Tokyo were destroyed by fire. He returned to England, setting up a new earthquake observatory at Shide Hill House. He caused something of a stir locally when he arrived with his Japanese wife Tone and assistant Mr Hirota. Reports flooded in from all over the world, and a steady flow of visitors came to see John and Tone, including Robert Falcon Scott – Scott of the Antarctic. The only visitors not welcome were members

Milne's earthquake observatory at Shide was visited by all sorts of people. Joining Tone and Milne (second left) is Robert Falcon Scott – 'Scott of the Antarctic' (far left).

of the press, who camped on the doorstep whenever any large earthquake had been detected.

In contrast to his importance in Japan, in Britain he was virtually ignored by the authorities. The Post Office refused to supply him with a time signal (synchronisation of signals being vital to accurate measurement). Eventually, in 1900 the Eiffel tower began to broadcast time signals, and a Mr Shaw set up a crystal receiver for Milne with an aerial between two elm trees.

In Shide, Milne was able to detect earthquakes so clearly that it became the world centre for seismology. To correct for local effects, he established a second instrument on the Island at Carisbrooke Castle. Another series of experiments was undertaken at Ryde, to try to establish the tilting of the sea-bed at high tide. Every week the trace showed huge swings, which confused Milne. Eventually he discovered that the signals did in a way record the earth moving since they coincided with times when the butler and the housekeeper were off duty at the same time. He further claimed that from the traces taken at Shide he could tell how long the gravel trucks were stationary at the Barley Mow pub.

Shide Hill House is not as it was in Milne's day. Much has been demolished or rebuilt, and a new extension obscures the outside of the great observatory. However, there is one relic of Milne. Inside the house, in what is now a spare bedroom, a plaque has been found under the wallpaper. Originally on the outside of the house, it reads 'Earthquake Observatory 1900', the only clue that this was once a world-class laboratory. After Milne's death in June 1913, the station was kept running for six years, but then the house was sold and Tone returned to Japan.

John Milne's home and laboratory are now part of a private house in Shide, but across the road, by the river, is the cherry tree planted in his honour by the Japanese ambassador.

Alexander Graham Bell and the Telephone

Alexander Graham Bell was born at 16 South Charlotte Street, on the corner of Charlotte Square, in Edinburgh, on 3 March 1847. His father and his grandfather were both authorities on elocution, and it wasn't long before the young Alexander was teaching people how to speak. He was enormously inventive, and not only made the first iron lung, but also bred special sheep with multiple nipples because he thought they would have more lambs. However, what makes him a legendary inventor is the telephone.

In 1863, at the age of sixteen, Alexander and his brother Melville began some serious research into how speech worked. They started with the anatomy of the mouth and throat and even examined the family cat (after it had died) so they could study the vocal cords in more detail. Studying the pitch of the vowel sounds, they imagined the throat and the mouth like two different-sized bottles. Each makes a different pitch, and they realised that the vowel sounds were a combination of two pitches. Their father, Melville senior, had spent years classifying vocal sounds and came up with a shorthand system called *Visible Speech*, where every sound was represented by a symbol. The idea was to teach the deaf to speak by putting all these sounds together.

They eventually made an elaborate speaking machine to test their theories. Later in 1863, Alexander went to Elgin near the Moray Firth in the north of Scotland to teach elocution at the Weston House Academy, and there, in what is now a Comet store, he first conceived the idea of transmitting speech with electricity.

When Alexander's two brothers died in 1870, the family moved to North America. Alexander settled in Boston, the scientific and academic centre of America, and was soon using Visible Speech to teach the deaf. The idea of transmitting speech along a wire never left him, and though he knew little about electricity he knew a good deal about speech and sound. His years of research led him up a few blind alleys, but by 1875 he had come up with a simple receiver that could turn electricity into sound: in other words, a speaker. It was essentially a magnet glued to a diaphragm, and able to move within a coil of wire, so that a change of electric current in the coil would cause the magnet, and therefore also the diaphragm, to move in or out. Thus a varying electrical signal produced a varying sound wave from the speaker.

But he still needed a transmitter. He had no effective way of converting the sounds of the voice into an electric signal. What he needed, as his assistant Tom Watson put it, was to 'generate voice-shaped electric undulations'. He tried a few weird contraptions, including a diaphragm connected to a needle. As he spoke into it, the needle dipped in and out of a bowl of acid. The varying resistance produced a varying electric current from a battery. The great breakthrough came quite by accident on 2 June 1875. Bell and Watson were testing a circuit with one transmitter and two receivers in separate rooms, when Bell switched off the transmitter. Then he heard a note coming from the receiver in his room. Puzzled by this, he went through, and found Watson adjusting the other receiver. Bell realised that, with the transmitter turned off, the note must be coming from the other receiver acting as a transmitter – in other words, as a microphone. At that moment, the telephone was born.

Bell inaugurates the New York to Chicago telephone service, 18 October 1892.

By a fluke, Bell had discovered that the receiver could also work in reverse – instead of making sound when he sent electricity through it, it made electricity when he supplied sound, because the sound moved the diaphragm, the diaphragm moved the magnet in the coil and this generated electricity. Six months went by before he was able to send intelligible speech down the wire, and according to popular legend, and Bell's diary, the first words ever spoken on the telephone were, 'Mr Watson, come here; I want to see you.' Rather peremptory, but no doubt the great man was excited, and no doubt Mr Watson jumped to it with alacrity.

Bell developed his system – he certainly needed a much better microphone – and submitted his patent on St Valentine's Day 1876, just two hours before Elisha Gray, his main rival. The patent was granted on 7 March, and was one of the most valuable patents ever issued. Over 600 lawsuits followed before a Supreme Court decision ruled in Bell's favour in 1893. Meanwhile, Bell had made the telephone available to the public in 1877, when the Bell Telephone Company was created. Developments were swift; within a year the first telephone exchange was built in Connecticut and within ten years more than 150,000 people had telephones in the United States alone. Bell married Mabel, the deaf daughter of his financial partner, and signed nearly all of his stock over to her, keeping just ten shares for 'sentimental reasons'. Within three years the price of Bell Telephone Company shares soared from fifty dollars to over a thousand dollars. Alexander was finally a man of independent means.

Bell eventually built a large house in remote Nova Scotia, where the landscape and weather reminded him of Scotland.

Here he continued his work with the deaf, including the young Helen Keller. He invented weird aircraft with wings based on triangles; he built a resuscitation device, the forerunner of the iron lung; and experimented with sheep. He had a peculiar notion that sheep with extra nipples would give birth to two or more lambs, and be more productive for farmers. He built Sheepville, a huge village of sheep pens, and spent years counting sheep nipples. The work continued for decades before the US State Department announced that there was no link between extra nipples and extra lambs.

Alexander Graham Bell was kind and generous and gave much of his money and time to improving the lives of those around him. He died in 1922 and will be revered for his work with the deaf and celebrated for his invention of the telephone.

There's a plaque on the wall of the house where he was born, 16 South Charlotte Street, Edinburgh, and a little sign on a pillar in the Comet store in Elgin – and many telephone companies still carry the name of Bell.

The 'Very Nearly Successful' Submarine of George William Garrett

We were both intrigued and sympathetic when we first heard about a steam-powered submarine that was 'very nearly successful'. It was designed and built by an Irish vicar, George William Garrett.

Garrett was born in Dublin and went to Trinity College. He became a curate in Moss Side, Manchester, and later an honorary commander in the Turkish Navy – Pasha Garrett. But what endears him to us is that in 1878 he established the Garrett Submarine, Navigation, and Pneumatophore Company, and in 1879 he designed and built the world's first mechanical submarine – powered by steam. She was 45 feet long and carried a crew of three. The boiler was stoked while she was on the surface, and then the fires were damped down and she submerged, using diving rudders. In theory she could stay under water for four hours, and do 10 miles at two or three knots, using latent heat to supply power. Garrett had a dream that hundreds of his submarines would form a defensive ring around the British coastline.

The Navy recognised her potential, especially in view of the impending war against the Russians.

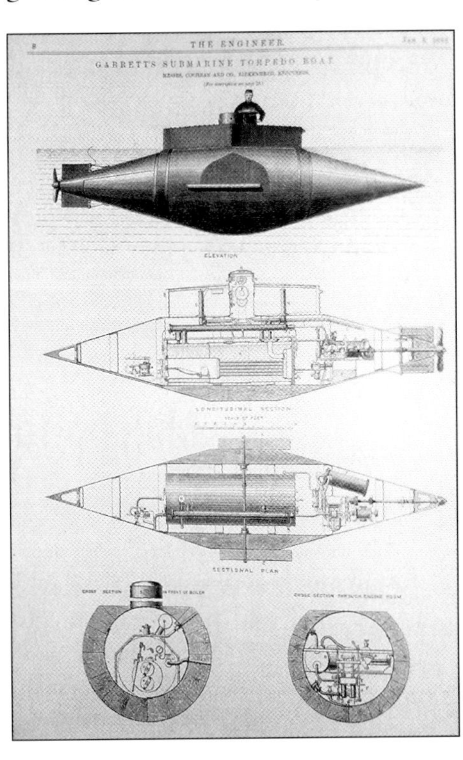

The *Resurgam* was described as 'very nearly successful' – not quite good enough for a submarine.

They offered Garrett £60,000 if the submarine passed marine trials in Portsmouth. So he organised a parish fête to raise funds, built his submarine, and launched her from Birkenhead. Unfortunately the weather was seriously bad and she ran into a storm off Rhyl in North Wales. The crew were taken off by lifeboat, and the submarine sank. She was called *Resurgam*, which is Latin for 'I will rise again' – but unfortunately she never did.

However, at Christmas 1995 divers found the submarine lying about 50 feet down on the seabed, with the hull intact and apparently in good condition. She has been declared a Maritime Treasure; so perhaps one day she will live up to her name.

Resurgam lies in 50 feet of water off North Wales.

Henry Hunnings' Telephone Microphone

York is a Roman city, a centre of learning – and just the sort of place I expected to find heroic pioneers. Furthermore, in Victorian times clergymen often dabbled in science; they were well educated and reasonably well paid, and they often had time on their hands. However, I was surprised to discover that a major advance in telecommunications was made in the tiny village of Bolton Percy, a few miles west of York, by the curate there – a man called Henry Hunnings. Life in small villages often revolved around the church, and as curate Hunnings was involved in weddings, funerals, and vital decisions such as whether or not to prevent the sexton from buying oil for the bells without the sanction of the churchwarden.

Meanwhile in Boston, Massachusetts, expatriate Scot Alexander Graham Bell was working with deaf people, and trying to develop hearing aids, such as the system of *Visible Speech* invented by his father. As an extension of this work, he looked for ways to transmit speech along wires, and in 1875 invented the telephone.

Unfortunately it didn't work very well at first, because at both ends he had what we would call a speaker, and speakers aren't really sensitive enough for the voice; so he had to shout to be heard in the next room and, although exciting, it wasn't very practical. Then along came Thomas Alva Edison, possibly the greatest inventor of all time, who produced a mouthpiece made out of compressed soot (or lampblack). Unfortunately that didn't work terribly well either.

At this point Henry Hunnings had a brilliant idea. We don't know how he knew about the telephone and the problems of getting speech into it, but he thought that maybe Edison should have used not soot, but bigger chunks of carbon. So Hunnings got hold of some charcoal and crushed it to make big granules. He put the granules between two thin metal plates or diaphragms to make a sandwich, and connected a battery across the two diaphragms. The idea was that the pressure of sound waves from the voice would push the diaphragms together and lower the electrical resistance, so more current would flow in the circuit.

That's the principle of the Hunnings microphone. The compressing of the chunks of carbon lowers the resistance, so that each bit of voice causes a pulse of current to flow in the circuit, and this can be sent as a signal along a wire. The weird thing is that anyone who knew anything about electricity couldn't possibly have invented this, because it seems to be obvious that no voice pressure could be high enough – you'd never shout loudly enough to be able to move those great chunks of carbon about. However, he was confident enough to patent his device in September 1878.

Hunnings tested his microphone on the telegraph wires between York and Darlington, and held a public demonstration of the 'micro-telephone' (price 15 guineas) at Cleveland Institute of Engineers, and it turned out to work extremely well. So well, in fact, that Alexander Graham Bell sued Hunnings – and lost. Eventually Bell bought the rights from Henry Hunnings for a thousand pounds. Not bad for a humble curate living in Bolton Percy.

And what an invention! The carbon-granule microphone remained in use until it was replaced by electronic systems in the 1980s; thus, in every telephone handset, the improbable genius of Henry Hunnings lived on for more than a hundred years.

If you have a little electrical meter you can easily make a model to see how the carbon-granule microphone works. First make a teaspoonful of carbon granules from a barbecue briquette (or artist's charcoal) by bashing it with a hammer. Lay a thin layer of granules on a 2p or 50p coin. Lay another coin on top. Make a circuit with a battery, the two coin-diaphragms, and the meter, set to measure current at its most sensitive setting. Then, while watching the meter, press on the top coin with your thumb, and see how the current increases with the pressure.

Bolton Percy is a pretty village with a lovely church, and a phone box within sight, but there is no plaque to commemorate the forgotten curate.

Concrete and Spiritualism: Andrew Thomas Turton Peterson

Peterson had an unconventional childhood. On the death of his parents he was brought up by the Revd John Michelle, his great-uncle, a clergyman and mechanical genius, and by his grandfather, Sir Thomas Turton Peterson, a baronet.

Curiously Andrew ran away to sea, where he might have stayed but for illness, which forced him to return home. He became a lawyer and went to India, where he was leader of the Calcutta Bar. While there he became interested in building methods and in spiritualism, both of which proved vital for the later construction of the great tower.

He eventually retired to the New Forest, buying a house there originally called Drumduan, but renamed Arnewood Towers. He built several structures including a mansion near the village of Sway in Portland cement concrete, which he considered to be a marvellous material. Some of them have disappeared, but there is still a practice tower, a cottage, and some of the outbuildings have become a turkey farm.

Portland cement was invented by Joseph Aspdin from Leeds, and is made by baking a mixture of chalk and clay at 1400°C. The resulting mixture reacts with water, setting hard even under water. However, it is not very strong and was originally intended as a decorative material only – it is called Portland cement because Aspdin claimed that when used as a render on brick buildings it resembled Portland stone. Subsequently it was found that when mixed with sand it would make an excellent mortar for sticking bricks together, and that when aggregate such as gravel or pebbles was added, it made enormously strong concrete.

Concrete is actually a very old building material. The oldest concrete was found in Lepenski Vir in former Yugoslavia, and is dated at 5600 BC. The technique was then lost but taken up again by the Romans. The height of Roman concrete technology is the Pantheon in Rome – built of lightweight concrete in AD 127 and still standing today. It isn't quite clear when Peterson started to build the tower, but it was under construction in 1879 when the Tay Bridge at Dundee collapsed. A slightly nervous Peterson consulted an engineer who reassured him that his design would withstand 56 lb per square foot – more than any wind it would encounter in the New Forest.

He built entirely without scaffolding, instead using three wooden moulds each 6 inches high; when the three moulds were full of concrete, the lower one was removed, relocated to the top of the growing tower, and then filled again. Suitable aggregate seems to have been a problem, and in 1884 he

Concrete cottages constructed by Peterson in Sway village, with the practice tower visible on the right..

wrote 'Shingle matter becoming serious . . . enquire about the beach', and indeed he did raid the local beach.

The design is very impressive, and here he had some help. He decided to consult Sir Christopher Wren, the architect of St Paul's Cathedral. Unfortunately Sir Christopher had been dead for 156 years, but this wasn't a problem because Peterson had the services of William Lawrence, an uneducated labourer, who was his medium. Lawrence was able to contact great artists and make 'spirit drawings'. They published a book, *Essays from the Unseen, delivered through the mouth of W.P., a sensitive, and recorded by ATTP*. Sir Christopher Wren apparently drafted the design for the tower – curiously it is gothic in design, a form Wren disliked in life. Perhaps he had come round to the idea in the intervening 156 years . . .

Peterson wanted to prove that concrete was a serious structural material, and despite all the weird seances and so on, the tower is a brilliant demonstration of what concrete can do. He also had another motive. The 1870s saw a serious depression in agriculture, wages were very low and there was terrible unemployment. The tower employed local farm workers for seven years, and Peterson paid well over the usual rate for labour. When he died in London in 1906 at the age of ninety-three, his remains were cremated and the urn containing his ashes was brought to Sway to rest in the vault under the tower – on a concrete table.

Peterson's greatest creation is the Sway tower, now a private dwelling – so please don't disturb the occupants. There is no access but it can be viewed from just off the A337 near Hordle. Park on Flexford Lane near the Cattery.

Let There Be Light! Joseph Wilson Swan and Perfecting the Electric Light Bulb

Thomas Alva Edison probably deserves the title 'World's Greatest Inventor'. But despite his own claims and those of many American books, he did not invent the electric light bulb. That distinction belongs to Joseph Swan, a chemist from the north-east of England, working alone in his spare time.

Swan and Edison both knew there were immense rewards for the man who succeeded in applying the new great power source, electricity, to the universal desire to light every home. The struggle to do so took place in the courts as well as the laboratory, but eventually saw the two men come together.

By 1850 gas lighting had been around for forty years, and was common in shops and posh homes, but gas was smelly, poisonous and expensive. It was not all that bright, either: the gas mantle you may have seen on camping-gas lights, which glows with an intense greenish-white light, was still a long way off. In fact there was an electric light, the arc lamp – first used in Dungeness lighthouse in 1862. The arc lamp was an electric spark between two conducting rods connected to a battery. The trick lay in getting a constant arc, rather than spluttering sparks. This required the rods – usually of carbon – to be kept a constant distance apart, a problem since the rods are constantly burning away in the intense heat of the arc. In commercial applications, clever clockwork mechanisms were devised to first 'strike' the arc, by bringing the rods together, and then separating them to the right distance and maintaining the spark gap as the rods burned away.

These complications might have been overcome, but everyone knew the arc lamp would never become the universal electric light. Apart from the complexity, noise from the spark and the danger, they were too bright. If you had a lighthouse an arc lamp was fine, but as a bedside light it was seriously over-powered. However, the arc lamp defined the problem: it was quaintly called 'the subdivision of the electric light'.

Joseph Wilson Swan was born on 31 October 1828 at Pallion Hall in Sunderland. He left school when he was twelve, and was apprenticed to a firm of chemists, before taking up a position with John Mawson, a chemist in Newcastle. He invented several new processes for the developing photography business. In the 1840s Swan, a keen member of the Newcastle Literary and Philosophical Society, had seen a lecture at which electrical incandescence was demonstrated. A piece of wire was connected across a battery, and glowed orange. It was enough to make Swan think that incandescent lamps were the way to go. There is a problem: generally you either get no glow (wire too thick, battery too weak) or the wire burns out immediately. But if the wire survives, it is nowhere near bright enough to be a useful light. When the coil is glowing dull red, it's at about 700 or 800°C. At about 1000° it would glow yellow, but then the copper would melt. Swan tried a mixture of platinum and iridium, and managed to get the temperature up to about 2000°C before it melted, but he still wanted more.

So in his spare time from chemistry he experimented with all sorts of different materials. What we use now is the metal tungsten, but 130 years ago tungsten was both hard to obtain and impossible to work. So Swan chose carbon, which doesn't melt below 3500°C. What he wanted was tiny thin pieces, which he made by taking little strips of paper and carbonising them by toasting them gently in an oven without air. He tried all sorts of paper, and he tried spreading them with treacle and syrup and other stuff that goes black when you overcook it. Some of these worked a bit, and glowed brightly, but they were still awfully weak: he could not get consistent success. Although carbon doesn't melt, it burns easily if there is any oxygen about.

The solution seemed obvious: get rid of the oxygen. He tried pumping all the air out of his bulbs with the mercury pump that had just been invented, but this still did not work. There was enough oxygen adsorbed on the carbon – stuck to the outside – to burn it when it heated up. The stroke of genius which was to solve that problem took a while to come to Swan. Meanwhile, he tackled the unsatisfactory filaments themselves. He concluded that the fibrous nature of the paper he used was to blame, and decided to make his own material. The first artificial filaments were made by treating cotton with sulphuric acid, and later ones by dissolving blotting paper in zinc chloride and squirting it into alcohol to make long strings. These were in fact the first artificial fibres, precursors of rayon. He saw their potential, and asked his wife to crochet them into collars and doilies! They can be seen in the Newcastle Discovery museum.

By the late 1870s, when Swan had been working on the problem for a quarter of a century, everything was in place. He had his artificial filaments, carbonised in a furnace without air; the vacuum pump had been improved beyond recognition; and in 1878 he perfected a technique for getting rid of the adsorbed oxygen. When he had pumped all the air he could out of the glass bulb containing the filament, he carefully heated up the filament

Early Swan carbon-filament bulbs. (By permission of the President and Council of the Royal Society)

while still pumping. More oxygen came off the surface of the warm filament and was pumped away. For the first time, he could make his filament glow white, but not burn. He first demonstrated his successful lamp to a few people in January 1879, and then on 3 February 1879 to an audience of seven hundred people at the Literary and Philosophical Society of Newcastle upon Tyne. Swan's house, Underhill at Gateshead, was lit with his own light bulbs later the same year.

He patented the pumping process, but he thought the idea of making a filament lamp so obvious it wasn't worth patenting. He reckoned without Thomas Alva Edison. Swan's lamp first worked in February 1879. Four months earlier Edison had made a dramatic, sweeping claim that he had solved the problem of the electric light by using carbonised paper. His cable sent the price of gas shares tumbling on the Stock Exchange – and in October 1879 Edison patented the carbon-filament lamp. Swan sent a little note to the journal *Nature* saying that he had been making carbonised paper filaments for fifteen years – and it did not work. Edison went on to try fibres of carbonised bamboo, and imported it specially from Japan – but bamboo didn't work either.

In 1881 Swan started producing his carbon-filament light bulbs in a factory at Benwell, and Edison threatened to sue him for infringing his patent. Swan pointed out that he had been making these lamps before Edison applied for his patent. In the end they stopped arguing, joined forces, and formed the Edison & Swan United Electric Light Co.

Swan's most crucial work was done in the greenhouse at Underhill, now a residential home for the elderly.

Eadweard Muybridge, Who Settled a Bet by Snapping a Horse

He was born Edward Muggeridge in Kingston upon Thames in 1830, but changed his name to Eadweard (the Saxon spelling) Muygridge when he moved to New York. By the time he became a photographer, Muygridge had become Muybridge, and his transformation was complete. He became director of the photographic surveys of the United States government, and a celebrated landscape photographer. He might have remained so if he had not met the Governor of California, Leland Stanford, who was also president of the Central Pacific Railroad.

Stanford's passion was the breeding and training of racehorses, and there was a serious controversy about how a horse's feet move when it is trotting or cantering – the movement is too fast for the human eye. Stanford is supposed to have made a large bet supporting his theory that all four feet are off the ground at the same time when a horse gallops by. He reckoned that photography could help to prove the point, and hired Muybridge as photographer. his first efforts used a single camera, but his real success came when his 'special exposing apparatus' was connected to a series of still cameras.

Eadweard Muybridge brought moving pictures to the world.

Muybridge used for his subject Stanford's horse, Occident. He used various 'special exposing apparatuses', some mechanical and others electronic, but usually fired by a trip-wire. When he started out he had to be as much chemist as photographer, making his own extremely sensitive wet collodion plates and developing his pictures. The bright Californian sunshine helped in obtaining the very short exposures he needed, but even so his technical prowess was extraordinary. In some cases he got exposures as short as one six-thousandth of a second, a speed only found on specialist cameras even today. He worked out that for Occident he needed 24 cameras 21 inches apart to record the separate parts of the horse's stride. As Occident ran across the trip-wires, the horse pulled out a pin which allows the shutter to move and take a picture.

Stanford won his bet because the pictures clearly showed Occident and other horses with all four legs off the ground at the same time. In fact, the motion of the horse looked so strange that some people thought the pictures had been fixed in some way. But in truth, this was the first time that the motion could be properly analysed, and the representation of horses in motion in paintings and drawings had to change to fit Muybridge's new evidence.

While he was in California taking pictures of horses, Muybridge had some difficulty with his private life. He discovered that his wife Flora had been having an affair with a man called Harry Larkyns. Muybridge was so angry that he went to find Larkyns and shot him at point-blank range. He was put on trial but the jury decided the killing was entirely justified, and Muybridge walked free!

Muybridge came to the Royal Institution in March 1882 to lecture before the Prince of Wales, Alfred Lord Tennyson and other dignitaries. This was part of a tour on which he showed the first moving pictures in Europe. It had become clear, thanks to the work of Peter Paul Roget, the man who penned the famous thesaurus, that images persist in the eye for about a sixteenth of a second. If you showed a series of still images very quickly they would result in the illusion of continuous movement. The zoetrope, essentially a children's toy, had been invented in 1833 to show images of bouncing

The proof is in the trotting: one of Muybridge's series of horse studies which prove that trotting horses do have all four feet off the ground at the same time.

balls, dancers and so on. Muybridge now wanted to do the same for his photographic images.

He used a complicated projector he had invented – the zoopraxiscope – which had counter-rotating glass discs. One disc was a shutter, while the other carried his series of photographs. In fact, his photos had to be reproduced on the discs by artists, because the zoopraxiscope tended to squash normal pictures, so he had them re-drawn at double width to compensate. The results were stunning. For the first time audiences could see real, moving pictures. Some were at full speed, others slowed down to enable analysis of the movement, the forerunner of all the slow-motion replays we use today. Since he knew one of the men who went on to develop celluloid film, it seems that only the technology stopped Muybridge from inventing the cinema; he certainly laid its foundations.

He moved from horses to other kinds of animals, and then on to human subjects. His definitive work was *Animal Locomotion, an Electro-photographic Investigation of Consecutive Phases of Animal Movement, 1872–1885*. He usually insisted his human subjects were naked so that the movement could be better analysed – though what his Californian models thought of playing cricket with no clothes on is sadly unrecorded. He eventually moved back home to Kingston where his final project was to build a scale model of the Great Lakes in his garden.

The best place to see Muybridge artefacts is Kingston Museum, open from 10 a.m. to 5 p.m. daily. It's free. You can also access their webside: http://www.Kingston.ac.uk/muytext7/htm.

Augustus Desiré Waller: Toy Trains, Mercury and the ECG

A distinguished physiologist, Augustus Waller lived his life in the shadow of his father, and his reputation is obscured by that of Willem Einthoven, the Dutch physiologist who received a Nobel Prize for perfecting Waller's invention. Nevertheless there is no doubt that it was Augustus Desiré Waller who first made an extraordinary breakthrough in the medical use of the heart's electrical beats.

That curious middle name Desiré might have been hidden away, but Augustus Waller really had to use it to distinguish himself from his father, who was also called Augustus Waller, was also a physiologist, but had a different peculiar name: Volney. Waller senior was famous for a method of investigating nerve pathways that became known as 'Wallerian nerve degeneration'. Always worried about being compared unfavourably to his dad, Augustus Desiré commented 'I am the Wallerian degeneration'. A snappy dresser with a big personality and a wry sense of humour, he married Alice Palmer of the Huntley & Palmer biscuit family. One of his students wrote on the blackboard 'Waller takes the biscuit'.

Since the early days of electricity it had been known that muscles contract when stimulated by a small voltage. In the eighteenth century the Italian Luigi Galvani had noticed that frogs' legs twitch when touched with metal carrying a charge. However, it was not until 1842 that another Italian, physicist Carlo Matteucci, had shown that in animals an electrical current preceded every heartbeat. Not surprisingly investigating the heart's impulses became all the rage and eventually Waller joined in. The main difficulty was in detecting and recording the tiny electrical potentials. Waller chose a surprising device invented by Gabriel Lippmann, and known as the Lippmann electrometer. It was essentially a very narrow U-shaped tube of mercury, with sulphuric acid sitting on top of the mercury at one end. A tiny voltage would make the surface of the mercury move further up or down the tube. The result was hardly spectacular – you had to view it with a microscope – but it gave Waller the sensitivity he needed. He then had two inspired ideas.

He realised that what might be interesting about the electrical activity of the heart was how it changed over the period of a heartbeat. But to see this, he had to record the movement of his electrometer over time. His answer was toy trains. Because the mercury moved so little with each heartbeat, he magnified it by projecting it on to the wall, with a device rather like a slide projector. What you then saw was the rising and falling shadow of the mercury. He arranged for a photographic plate, attached to the carriage of a toy train, to travel across the light beam. The rising and falling shadow was then recorded as the first ever 'electrocardiogram' – a term invented by Waller.

This seems a great breakthrough, and was regarded as such, but then Waller had his second great idea. Until now, electrical activity could only be recorded from an *exposed heart*, by using electrodes applied to its surface through an opening in the chest. Waller wondered whether this activity could in fact be detected from outside the chest, by attaching electrodes to the skin. He experimented on himself, his family, and any other willing victims, trying electrodes in various places on the chest, back and various limbs. He eventually realised that the body is divided diagonally in a sort of circuit with the head and right arm connected to one side, the legs and left arm connected to the other. So by connecting electrodes to, say, the right hand and left leg, Waller was able to record his electrocardiogram. For convenience, he used metal basins filled with salt water as electrodes, so the subject simply had to dip a hand and a foot into the salty water to get a reading. He published the readings from Thomas Goswell, a technician in the laboratory, as *A demonstration on man of electromotive changes accompanying the heart's beat*, in 1887.

Augustus Waller was often accompanied by his bulldog, Jimmie, and used the rather handsome beast in some of his public demonstrations. One was at a 'Conversazione' of the Royal Society, where Jimmie willingly stepped into the jars of salt water as he had often done before, in order to display his electrocardiogram. This caused some amusement, and Jimmie ended up in the *Daily Mirror* as 'James, "the only scientific dog in England"'. However, the result was a rather curious anonymous letter to the *Lancet*. Under the heading 'A Heartless Experiment', it complained about the dog's 'ordeal by electricity'. Things really got out of hand when Mr Ellis Griffith, MP for Anglesey, raised a parliamentary question. The reply came from Mr Gladstone – not, sadly, the great Prime Minister, but his son who was a home office minister. Responding to the allegation that the dog might have experienced pain, and was made to stand in salt solutions, Gladstone replied that 'If my Honourable Friend has ever paddled in the sea, he will understand the sensation'.

Waller with Jimmie the bulldog, whose 'ordeal by electricity' provoked parliamentary questions.

As so often with pioneers of science, Waller was ahead of his time. The technology he had chosen was not really up to the job, and in order to work out what was happening in the heart the trace from Waller's machine had to be 'interpreted' using complex formulae. The problem was to do with the Lippmann electrometer: it simply wasn't fast enough. At one of Waller's lectures in 1889, Willem Einthoven was in the audience. He was hugely impressed, and went on to conduct experiments of his own. He eventually introduced the 'string galvanometer' which sounds a bit home-made but was actually a fantastically sensitive device for recording tiny voltages. He demonstrated the true shape of the heart's electrical waves, and in 1924 was awarded the Nobel Prize for Medicine for the discovery of the ECG. Waller had died two years previously and so was not eligible. So Einthoven had made the ECG into an everyday medical instrument, but the first electrocardiogram had certainly been recorded by Augustus Desiré Waller.

No places are specifically linked to Waller, but for medical history why not visit the Wellcome Centre for Medical Science at 183 Euston Road, London NW1 2BE. It's open Monday to Saturday but is closed on bank holidays.

John Boyd Dunlop and the Pneumatic Tyre

This is the apparently straightforward story of the vet who transformed cycling comfort by ripping up one of his wife's old dresses, nailing it to a wooden disc and thus inventing the pneumatic tyre. Unfortunately, Dunlop's claim to this great invention turns out to be rather controversial.

John Boyd Dunlop was born on 5 February 1840 in Dreghorn in Scotland. He studied animal medicine, and went to Belfast to set up as a vet in 1869. For twenty years he ran a successful practice in Gloucester Street. He had a son, Johnny, who rode to school on a tricycle and liked to race with his friends. But the streets in Belfast were rough – they were made of cobbles, with tramlines crossing them, and in those days bicycle and tricycle tyres were made of solid rubber. Anyone who has tried solid tyres will confirm that it would have been most uncomfortable. Young Johnny complained that his bottom was sore.

His dad John Boyd wondered if he could smooth the ride by putting a cushion of air between the bike and the road, and he decided to build a prototype. Apparently he was for some reason or other used to handling and using rubber, so he got hold of a thin rubber tube and glued the ends together with rubber solution. To inflate the tyre, he incorporated a valve from a football, and so made himself an inner tube. The next challenge was to fix the tyre to the rim of the wheel, and he achieved this, and protected the delicate rubber tube, thanks to one of his wife's old dresses, which he tore into strips and

Dunlop did not invent the pneumatic tyre – but he invented the first one that worked.

wrapped over the inner tube, nailing it into his prototype wooden wheel.

Then, rather brilliantly, he conducted a scientific test. He took his prototype wheel, and a similar one with a solid tyre, and rolled them along his cobbled back yard. The solid one soon fell over, but the pneumatic tyre rolled to the end and bounced off the back wall. So he made pneumatic tyres for the back wheels of Johnny's tricycle, and sent him off to school. The first field reports were highly favourable: Johnny could now beat his friends in races – and in comfort!

What was surprising was that the new tyre was not only more comfortable, it actually went faster. The reason the pneumatic tyre works so well is that the air cushion in effect irons out the little bumps in the road. Technically, it reduces the 'unsprung weight' to zero. When the solid wheel goes over a bump, the whole wheel (and thus the whole bike) is thrown into the air, which is uncomfortable for the rider and also uses energy. When the pneumatic tyre goes over the same bump, the tyre squashes a bit but doesn't rise. So you hardly feel a jolt, and although some energy is lost – and goes to heat the air inside the tube – it loses much less energy than is necessary to lift the bike and rider off the ground. The squishiness of the tyre does increase its rolling resistance, because every movement of the tyre on the road deforms the rubber – it's like riding up a very slight hill all the time – but you lose much less energy like this than you do if you have to lift the whole bike and rider on every bump.

John Boyd Dunlop thought there might be money in his tyre, so he demonstrated it to some Belfast businessmen, and then applied for a patent in July 1888. He got tyres made in Edinburgh, with bikes from Edlin and Co. in Belfast, who had made Johnny's tricycle. There were some real technical problems to be overcome, like getting special forks made to fit his chunky tyres. But the biggest problem was the macho attitude of cyclists; many serious cyclists thought only namby-pambies would ride on safety bicycles as opposed to the fast but deadly 'high bicycle' or penny-farthing, let alone on cushioned wheels. So Dunlop went straight to the top. Willie Hume, Captain of the Belfast Cruiser Cycle Club, had

The Dunlop Company went from bikes to cars and from strength to strength.

had a terrible fall from a penny-farthing so he rode safety bikes. Dunlop persuaded him not only to ride on pneumatic tyres but to enter a race with them. The great race happened on 18 May 1889, on the Queen's College playing fields. Everyone laughed at Willie Hume when he turned up on his inflatable tyres, but they stopped laughing when he won the race. Two of the losers in that race were the Du Cros brothers. They managed to get hold of bikes with pneumatic tyres, took them over to England, and in the summer of 1889 they won every race they were allowed to enter.

Their dad was William Harvey Du Cros, a Dublin paper merchant. He saw the potential in these tyres, and in 1896 he bought the business for three million pounds. After various deals and struggles it became the Dunlop Rubber Company, with the white-bearded portrait of John Boyd Dunlop as its logo. Tyres were at first still fixed to the rim of the wheel – conventionally spoked now, rather than wooden – by wrapping canvas impregnated with rubber solution round the inner tube and rim, permanently fixing the tyre. This skilled job was done by the company, so cycle manufacturers from England who wanted pneumatic tyres had to send men over on the ferry with bare rims to be fitted up. Dunlop himself took no part in the business, moving to Dublin where eventually he had an interest in a drapers. So although he lived comfortably, it was not Dunlop who made the real money from his invention.

This is where you have to be rather careful, because there is a dispute as to whether it is really 'his' invention at all. To the distress of the company, it turned out that Dunlop wasn't the first person to invent the pneumatic tyre; one had actually been patented forty-three years earlier by another Scot called Robert Thompson. So what are the facts? The titles of the patents reveal what the two men were trying to do. Thompson's patent is dated 10 December 1845, and is for 'An improvement in carriage wheels which is also applicable to other rolling bodies'. Dunlop's patent of 31 October 1888 is for 'An improvement in Tyres of wheels for bicycles, tricycles, or other road cars'. Thompson's wheels were big and heavy, intended for carriages. The problem was they were so cumbersome that the idea didn't catch on. In Dunlop's day the bicycle as we know it was just becoming available, and he saw this as the important area. Perhaps Thompson was just ahead of his time.

Both men described the use of a rubber tube encased in canvas, though only Dunlop specifies in detail how it is to be attached to the wheel, or how air is to be introduced (through a non-return valve). Thompson merely says that air is passed through a pipe 'fitted with an air-tight screw cap'; he doesn't say how you stop air escaping as you tighten it. In summary, the idea of a pneumatic tyre was clearly patented first by Thompson, although we have Dunlop to thank for the word 'pneumatic'. Dunlop thought of applying it to bicycles and other light vehicles, where Thompson had rather generally applied it to locomotives, carriages and other road vehicles. Dunlop subsequently modified his patent, to make it clear that he was claiming the method for making and using the tyre, not the idea of using air.

So Dunlop's invention looks a little tainted – especially if you believe the claim of some supporters of Thompson that the families actually knew each other in Scotland. But it seems unlikely Dunlop would have applied for a patent knowing that someone else had already taken one out – indeed you might have expected the Patent Office to have picked this up. In the end, it was Dunlop rather than Thompson who brought the world the pneumatic tyre, thanks in part to his sore-bottomed son.

The premises of John Boyd Dunlop's veterinary practice have become a car park, but the pneumatic tyre is everywhere.

Margaret Huggins, Who Helped to Show What Stars Are Made of

Despite a woman being on the throne, the Victorian age was not a time when women flourished in science. The Royal Society did not admit women fellows, and when for instance it wanted to hear of the work of Marie Curie, the paper had to be given by her husband. But it is clear that many women were involved in science, although their work was often lost – published under the name of their husband or professor. Margaret Huggins' story is known perhaps because her contribution was so very great, and because she was lucky enough to live on into the twentieth century. Even so, all the papers on astronomy to which she contributed have Sir William's name at the top, and it was he who received the knighthood and medals. But between them, Margaret and William Huggins revolutionised our view of the universe.

Margaret Lindsay Murray was born in Dublin in 1848. Her mother died when she was only a child, and she spent a lot of time with her grandfather, who taught her about stars and constellations. She even studied sun-spots systematically from the age of ten. Most interestingly, considering what followed, she made her own spectroscope. Simply put, this is a device for analysing the spectrum of light. It was being applied to the chemistry of flames because the different atoms in a flame emit light of very characteristic colours. Spot these colours and you can say what atoms are present. It has been suggested that Margaret introduced the spectroscope to William Huggins, though it is clear he was using one from the 1860s, and they were not married until 1875.

Whoever thought of it, the application of the spectroscope to the telescope was one of the great breakthroughs in astronomy, because it let you do chemistry at a distance of millions of miles. By analysing the light of stars, you see what atoms were burning in them. The Huggins were the first to show that stars are made of the same elements we know here on earth.

Margaret Huggins (1848–1915).

A particularly puzzling and at the time controversial feature of the night sky was the nebulae. Margaret is best known for her work on the Orion Nebula. You can see Orion any clear night in the winter. Look towards the south and he is the hunter, with a belt of three stars and a sword of three stars hanging from it. If you look carefully with a telescope at Orion's sword, around the middle star you can see a sort of smudge. Smudges like this are called nebulae, because they look nebulous – like hazy clouds. Other astronomers observed many nebulae, and thought they were all clusters of distant stars. They included the Earl of Rosse, who built the biggest telescope in the world in an attempt to see the stars in nebulae – but Margaret was not convinced. In 1889 she turned her telescope on the Orion Nebula, and used her spectroscope to look at the spectrum of the light coming from it. Some nebulae give spectra that look like a star's, and she was familiar with them, but the Orion Nebula gave quite a different result – just a single bright green line.

Here is William's rather over-heated account of another nebula observation. This is of a 'planetary nebula', so called because they resembled the discs of planets rather than points of light like stars: 'I directed the telescope for the first time to a planetary nebula in Draco. The reader may now be able to picture to himself to some extent the feeling of excited suspense, mingled with a degree of awe, with which, after a few moments of hesitation, I put my eye to the spectroscope. Was I not about to look into a secret place of creation? I looked into the spectroscope. No spectrum such as I expected! A single bright line only!'

A huge argument developed between William Huggins and Norman Lockyer, another astronomer who thought the green line was from magnesium. Meteorites are full of magnesium so Lockyer thought nebulae were made up of meteorites. But Margaret's brilliant photography, keen eye, and her immense dedication proved that the green line was something new, the spectrum of a gas. They called this unknown 'new' element nebulium, but modern astronomy has since shown it to be a rare form of superheated oxygen. She concluded that there are two types of nebulae. Some *are* clusters of distant stars, but some, including Orion, are clouds of gas or dust, being heated by an unseen source within; they may even be stars in the process of being formed from clouds of dust.

The Huggins heard about the work of Doppler, whose 'Doppler shift' makes the note of an ambulance siren go up as it approaches and down as it goes away. The same can be applied to light, though you see not a change in note but a moving of lines in the spectrum. Looking at the star Sirius, they concluded that it was moving away from the earth at 25 miles a second, an extraordinary conclusion and evidence that would later be used by Edwin Hubble to show that the universe is expanding.

Margaret herself was quite cheerful about the prevailing attitude towards women. She said in 1905: 'I find that men welcome women scientists provided they have the proper knowledge. It is absurd to suppose that anyone can have useful knowledge of any subject without a great deal of study. When women have really taken the pains thoroughly to fit themselves to assist or to do original work, scientific men are willing to treat them as equals. It is a matter of sufficient knowledge.'

Although memorials to the Huggins are scarce on earth, you could visit the Lunar Crater Huggins, or the one on Mars, or perhaps minor planet 2635 – also known as Huggins.

Mikael Pedersen and Bikes Tied together with String

The *Dursley Gazette* for 21 October 1893 reported:

A NEW BICYCLE

> Mr M. Pedersen of Dursley, with that ingenuity for which he is known, has recently constructed a safety bicycle of remarkable character. Its weight is only 19 pounds and the maker has tested the strength in an extraordinary way, he having ridden it up Whiteway.

Whiteway is the fearsome hill that rises through the beech woods to the east of Dursley in Gloucestershire. It is one of those hills that if you ride up it on a bicycle you wish you hadn't! In 1896 the Cyclists Touring Club instructed a local wheelwright to put up a sign on Whiteway reading: notice to cyclists. this hill is dangerous. Certainly I should not like to come down it without brakes and with my feet on the handlebars, which was the style in Pedersen's day.

Mikael Pedersen was born on 25 October 1855 near Copenhagen in Denmark, the eldest of seven children. He became an apprentice in a local firm making agricultural equipment, and while he was there invented a self-clearing threshing machine and a new bicycle, the parts for which were made in the factory. He also invented a centrifugal cream separator, which made him money and got him invited to England by Mr Lister of Dursley. He moved over to England

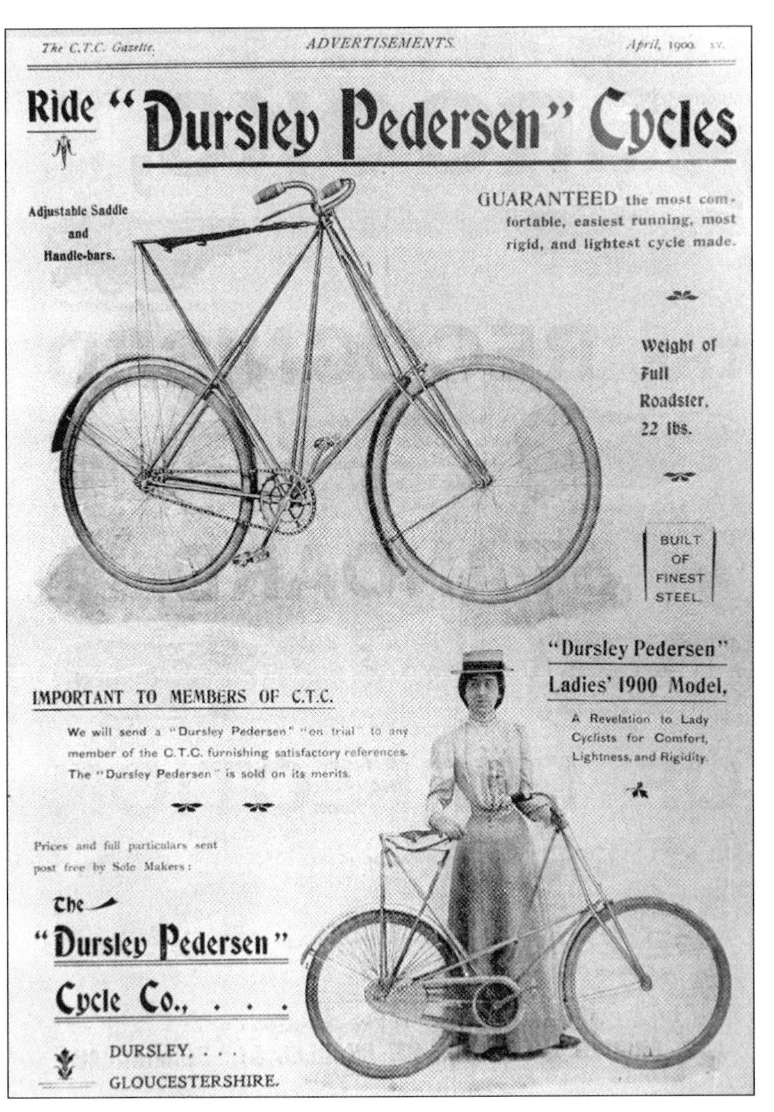

The unlikely but ingenious Pedersen cycle. You sat on a sling which tensioned the slender frame.

in March 1893, and in September the same year patented his new bicycle.

Behind his house he set up a small factory to make bicycles; the early machines were made of wood, but in 1897 he switched to metal. The startling new concept behind Pedersen cycles was that they were all in tension. The frame was made of many very thin tubes, most of which seemed to meet at a point behind the handlebars, and the ends of the tubes were tied together with fine wires. Even the saddle, instead of being perched on the end of a rigid saddle tube, was slung on a hammock-like strap, which provided the rider with soft suspension.

Soon these new cycles began to make their mark. On 14 November 1898 Harry Goss Green set a new record on a Pedersen from London to Brighton and back in 6 hours, 8 minutes and 11 seconds. In 1900 he broke several more records: London–Liverpool (203 miles) in 11 hours; World 100 miles in 4 hours 41 minutes; London–York (197.5 miles) in 10 hours 19 minutes; and World 12 hours, 225 miles.

Many other remarkable tales arose, such as that of the Revd Sidney Swan, who rode from his parish in Carlisle all the way to London (301 miles) in less than twenty-four hours, even though he was cut and bruised when knocked off by a dog near Towcester. Many thousands of Pedersen cycles were made in Dursley, and some are still being made today, both in England and on the continent.

In 1896 Mikael was President of the Dursley Star rugby football club and the Dursley Star cricket club. He married three times – to Laura, Dagmar, and Ingeborg. Unfortunately the business eventually failed, and he went back to Denmark, where he died on 22 October 1929. But his bones were brought back to Dursley in 1996.

A blue plaque marks Pedersen's house in Dursley, and Pedersen bicycles are still obtainable, both modern replicas and originals.

Liborio Pedrazzolli and his Swimming Umbrellas

People have always wanted to be able to flash through the water with more speed and more freedom; hence the attraction of flippers, snorkels and other swimming aids. Among the more splendid inventions in this area were the swimming umbrellas dreamed up by Liborio Pedrazzolli.

Mr Pedrazzolli came over to England from Italy in about 1880, married an English girl, and set himself up in business as a wholesale and export looking-glass manufacturer at 11 Hoxton Street in north-east London. He must have reflected carefully about improving the efficiency of his swimming, and reasoned that he got a good push on the water when he kicked with his feet, but his hands seemed to slip through almost without pulling him forwards. So in 1896 he applied for a patent for mini-umbrellas to hold in his hands and increase their grip on the water. His patent describes how they work: 'When the forward stroke takes place in swimming the apparati close up and thereby offer a minimum

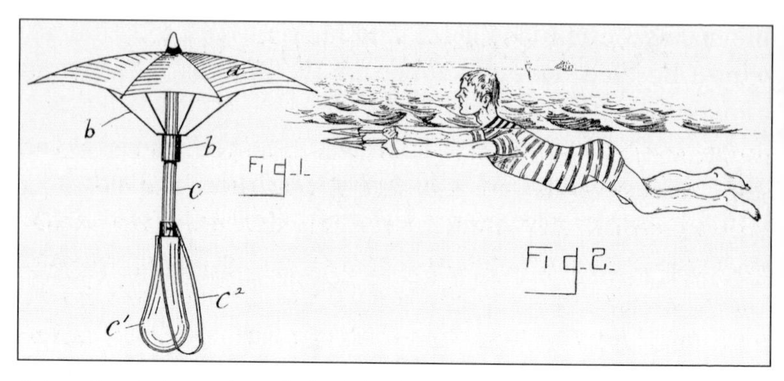

Pedrazzolli's patent swimming umbrellas: 'when the return stroke is made the apparati expand in umbrella form, and the resistance thus offered enables the swimmer to pull or propel himself through the water at a speed hitherto impossible'.

amount of resistance to the water, but when the return stroke is made the apparati expand in umbrella form, and the resistance thus offered enables the swimmer to pull or propel himself through the water at a speed hitherto impossible.'

There was only one way to test them; I made some myself. The result was interesting, although not conclusive. They certainly did give a good grip on the water, but only after about 12–13 inches of the stroke, because they were quite slow to open. Meanwhile they slightly impeded all hand movements, so my hands tired more quickly. After practising for half an hour I decided I would be better off without them – but perhaps if they had been lighter in construction, and a little longer, and I had persevered, I too might have been able to swim at a speed hitherto impossible!

What were Pedrazzolli's premises in Hoxton Street have become a school.

Poetic Doctor Ronald Ross

Jungle fever, Indian fever and malaria are three names for the same disease. Today in Asia and Africa there are still 100 million cases, and about a million deaths a year from malaria; in the nineteenth century the problem was far worse, extending to North and South America and many parts of Europe. What Ronald Ross came to know as the 'Indian fever problem' was truly one of the most urgent tasks facing medical science, though very little was known about the disease.

Ronald Ross was born in India and spent much of his adult life there, so malaria was very familiar to him – I was going to say 'in his blood', but you know what I mean. Like many sons of the English in India (his father was a general in the Indian Army) he was sent home aged eight to be educated. He seems to have liked many things – zoology, poetry, art – and wanted to be an artist. Dad, however, had other ideas and Ronald dutifully applied to become a doctor. For some reason he failed one of the two final exams – for admittance the Royal College of Physicians – and couldn't practise until he retook the exam. Curiously, there was a loophole that allowed him to become a ship's surgeon, and that is what he did for a year or so, crossing the Atlantic many times. Finally in 1880 he passed the crucial exam and got a job with the Indian Medical Service. This wasn't exactly a taxing time for Ronald, since he had time to learn polo and several languages while holding down his post. He also studied bacteriology, reinforced by a course he took on a return trip to England in 1889, during which he also met and married his wife, Rosa. His new skill with the microscope was to prove crucial. Shortly after this he wrote 'my studies on malaria did not advance' – the first mention of his work on the disease.

The transformation of Ross from run-of-the-mill colonial doctor to leading malaria researcher seems to have happened at a meeting in London with Patrick Manson on 10 April 1894. Thirteen years his senior, Manson would nevertheless have had a lot in common with Ross: both were qualified doctors, both had spent much time in the tropics. Manson however was already established as a tropical disease researcher, having shown that the organisms that caused elephantiasis are sucked up by mosquitoes and spend at least part of their life cycle in the insect. He thought that when infected mosquitoes died in water, they polluted the water and the next person became infected when they drank it. Manson wondered if the mosquito might be involved in malaria too.

Anopheles mosquitoes feed on human blood.

Although its name means 'bad air', the more modern view was that malaria transmission was by 'bad water' – Ross called the disease 'malacqueous'. Crucially, Manson knew the latest scientific theories about malaria, and set about educating Ross, showing him the latest microscopic evidence. In 1880 the French scientist Laveran had been looking at little black grains in blood-smears of malaria patients. To his surprise, one of these black specks sprouted tentacles.

Laveran recognised them as protozoa, and speculated that these must be the cause of malaria. When he showed them to visiting Italian scientists, they published the discovery themselves and gave the creature a name – *Plasmodium malariae*. Ross was amazed by the evidence in the blood, and took on Manson's suggestion that mosquitoes might be involved. But how could you prove it? Manson hoped that the younger Ross might be the man to do it.

Ross left England on 28 March 1895 full of enthusiasm. On the way he practised his dissection technique on the ship's cockroaches. Immediately on arrival in Bombay he rushed off to a hospital to take blood from a malaria patient – and succeeded in finding *Plasmodium*. However, his initial experiments in Hyderabad failed; he did not appreciate that *Plasmodium* only lives in a particular type of mosquito, and his was the wrong type. Bangalore, where he went to deal with a cholera outbreak, also had the wrong mosquitoes. The only ones with the parasite were what he called 'dapple-winged' mosquitoes, now called Anopheles. He felt a real sense of urgency – he and Manson wanted to beat the Italians, and he had a couple of months head-start before the mosquito season in Italy.

Ross decided to conduct an experiment. On 16 August 1897 he took a number of adult mosquitoes that had emerged from larvae the day before. The mosquitoes were fed on the blood of a malarious patient, Husein Khan, who was paid the princely sum of 10 annas (1 anna per mosquito). It works out at less than a penny – but money well spent, as it turned out.

Ross then began a procedure of daily dissections of these mosquitoes. On the fourth day he dissected the last but one mosquito and found large cells in the stomach wall. The next day in the last mosquito the cells had grown yet bigger. He had proved that the parasite, taken by the insects from the blood of an infected patient, could live and multiply in the Anopheles mosquito. Ross was so excited he wrote a poem:

> This day relenting God
> Hath placed within my hand
> A wondrous thing; and God
> Be praised. At His command,
>
> Seeking His secret deeds
> With tears and toiling breath,
> I find thy cunning seeds,
> O million-murdering Death.
>
> I know this little thing
> A myriad men will save.
> O Death, where is thy sting,
> Thy victory, O Grave!

However, despite the poetics Ross had not yet done it. He knew now that malaria parasites can get from man into mosquito, but how did they get back into man – by water or mosquito bite? This was an experiment he could not perform on patients, but he heard about some work on bird malaria. In June 1898 while in Calcutta, he performed the experiment. On the 25th, Ross took mosquitoes fed on infected birds and let them re-feed on uninfected birds. The new birds became infected. Then on 28 June, Ross reported to Manson that he had found 'germinal rods' in the stomach lining cells

Ross in Calcutta. He said the Indian fever problem would never be solved by a 'coup de microscope' – but that is exactly what he did.

in mosquitoes. On the 29th he found them in the blood cavity and by 4 July he had them in the salivary glands. In his letter to Manson on 9 July he said, 'I think I may now say QED'. In other words, Ross had shown how malaria parasites are taken into the stomach of the mosquito, multiply, and travel to the saliva glands where they enter the saliva, and eventually the victim when the mosquito bites. Manson announced Ross' work that same month.

The rival Italians came to a similar conclusion, and there was a row about who had done it first, eventually won by Ross. He returned to England for good, to a job found for him by Manson at the new Liverpool School of Tropical Medicine. Ross was so pleased with his discovery that he wrote to the new Nobel Foundation, wondering how he might get one of their prizes. They pointed out that he had to be nominated by someone else, which duly happened in time for the second set of prizes in 1902. Sadly, Ross seemed keener to take credit for himself than to acknowledge the immense help and support he had had from Patrick (later Sir Patrick) Manson. Despite the unpleasantness, Ross had made a huge discovery and a campaign began to eliminate the Anopheles mosquito and control the disease. Ross himself was knighted in 1911.

There are no places specifically linked to Ross, but again the Wellcome Centre for Medical Science, 183 Euston Road, London NW1 2BE, houses a great deal of biomedical and veterinary science history.

Dr Gaddes and Boiling the Perfect Egg

Different people have different problems at breakfast, and Dr Thomas Gaddes, dentist of Station Parade, Harrogate, was clearly worried about being called away – perhaps by demanding patients – before he could take his eggs out of the boiling water, so they became as hard as rocks. So in the late 1890s he devised an automatic egg-boiler, which actually took the egg out of the boiling water at the moment when it was perfectly cooked.

The diagrams he provided in his patents show the simplicity of the idea. The regulator h is adjusted on the lever arm into notch H, M, or S, according to whether you like

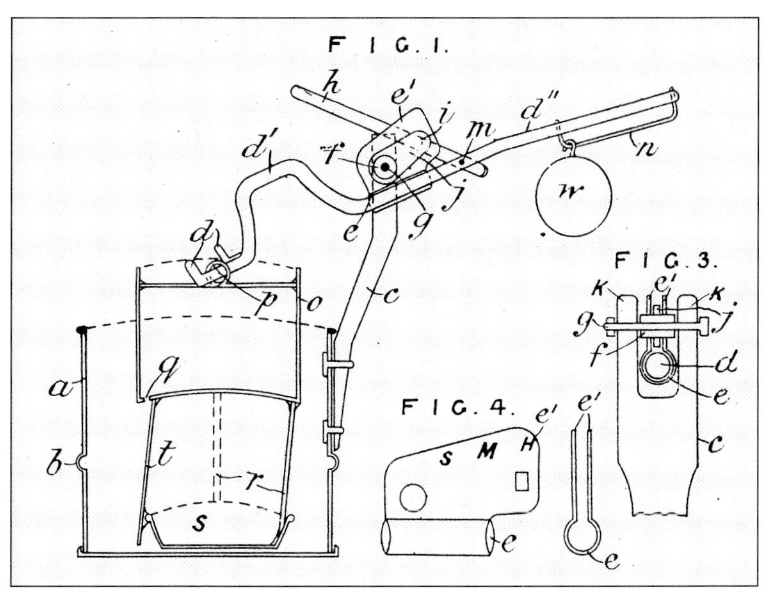

Dr Gaddes' automatic egg-boiler. The egg sits in the container 'S', shown in the cooking position. He simplified the design a year or two later.

your egg hard, medium, or soft, and the sliding weight is moved to the top slot if two eggs are to be boiled. Water trickles out of the reservoir, so that the basket holding the egg slowly rises. When enough water has run out, the slots in regulator h tip just below the horizontal, the weight slides down, and the egg is pulled rapidly out of the water. Indeed the egg is then slightly cooled by the water which continues to drain, so that it rapidly stops cooking.

Thomas Gaddes' premises at 104 Station Parade, Harrogate, are still there.

Frank Hornby and Meccano

Frank Hornby was born in Liverpool on 15 May 1863 at 77 Copperas Hill Road, which is now opposite Lime Street station, and just behind the Adelphi Hotel. He became a book-keeper at a company that imported meat and livestock at 17 James Street. He married Clara Godefroy in 1887, and within three years they had two sons, Roland and Douglas. As the boys began to toddle Frank made toys for them, using his few tools and lots of determination, apparently inspired by Samuel Smiles's book, *Self Help*, which recounts tales of the heroic feats achieved against massive odds by great engineers and industrialists through hard work and dedication.

Gradually, as the boys grew, the toys became more complex; Frank and his sons constructed miniature bridges and trucks from tinplate, but for each new model they had to start from scratch. What Frank wanted was to find a way of changing them – that is, making a variety of toys from one box of materials. He realised he would need parts that were interchangeable, and during a train journey he dreamed up the idea of using perforated strips. He developed the notion, and came up with a half-inch wide strip of metal with a hole every half inch. Combined with small nuts and bolts, thick wire for axles, and simple brass wheels, this made a flexible system suitable for the construction of a vast range of mechanical models.

He patented his idea in 1901, having to borrow the £5 patent fee from his employer, David Elliott. He called the kit *Mechanics Made Easy*, and sold the first sets for 7*s* 6*d*. They

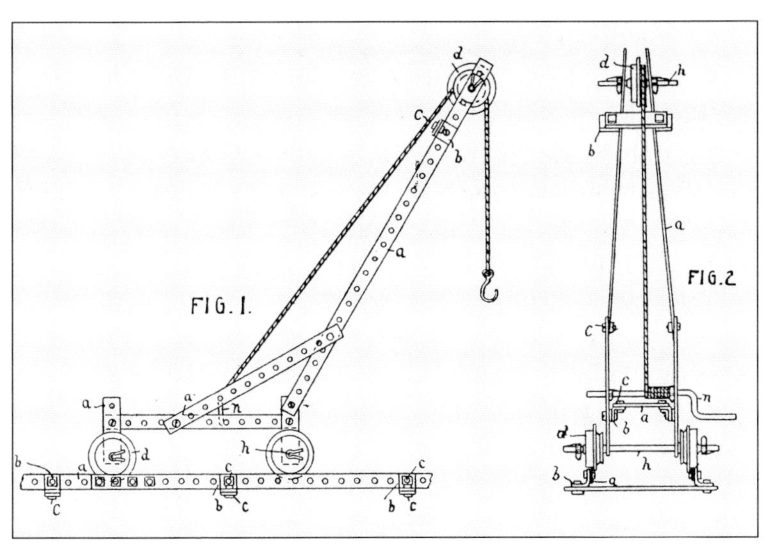

Hornby had to borrow £5 to take out his Meccano patent.

contained eighteen pages of instructions explaining how to build twelve models, including the Eiffel Tower and various bridges and cranes. Also included in the first booklet were eight pages of Hornby's introduction to the system. He claimed, 'The aimlessness of an undeveloped fancy will give way to an organised method, and from confused, hazy ideas will spring order and precision.'

A model-building competition was announced in the magazine *Model Engineer* in October 1903 and held in January 1904. The first production factory was opened in 1907 at 10 Duke Street, Liverpool, and Frank changed the name to Meccano. The kits steadily grew as he added gears, pulleys, cranks and clockwork motors. They became increasingly popular, and by 1920 he had more than 1,200 employees. This made Frank a wealthy man and he bought a big house in Maghull, Quarry Brook. In 1920 he introduced Hornby 0-gauge model trains, and in 1934 Dinky toys; in fact, he provided the same sort of enthusiasm and inspiration for young engineers as Arthur Ransome did for young sailors. In 1931 Frank Hornby became MP for Everton.

Frank Hornby died on 21 September 1936, and although children now spend much more time sitting in front of computer and television screens than they do making models, Meccano is still among the best-known and best-loved constructional toys, after almost 100 years.

Further Reading

The best single source of information about our Victorian heroes is the *Dictionary of National Biography*, published by Oxford University Press. The entries are brief and accurate. We research many other publications, and the list is far too long to be accommodated here, but this will give you some starting points if you wish to follow up some of the interesting characters we have touched on in this book.

You might find a trip to the library worthwhile if any of these titles prove elusive.

GENERAL BOOKS

Brown, G.I., *The Guinness History of Inventions*, Guinness, 1996
Cardwell, Donald, *The Fontana History of Technology*, Fontana, 1994
Clark, Donald (ed.), *The Encyclopedia of Inventions*, Marshall Cavendish, 1977
Robertson, Patrick, T*he Shell Book of Firsts*, Ebury Press, 1974
Rolt, L.T.C., *Great Engineers*, Bell, 1974
Smiles, Samuel, *Lives of the Engineers*,
Williams, Trevor I., *Our Scientific Heritage*, Sutton, 1996

INDIVIDUAL HEROES

Bessemer, Sir Henry, *An Autobiography, Engineering*, 1905
Gould, M.P., *Frank Hornby*, 1915
Irving, G., *The Devil on Wheels* [Kirkpatrick MacMillan], 1986
McClintock, Jean, *History of the Pneumatic Tyre*, 1923
McHale, Des, *George Boole, his Life and Work*, Boole Press, 1985
Mackay, James, *Sounds out of Silence: A Life of Alexander Graham Bell*, Edinburgh Mainstream, 1997
Moore, *Doris Langley, Ada, Countess of Lovelace*, 1997
Penrose, Harald, *An Ancient Air* [Stringfellow], Airlife, 1988
Rolt, L.T.C., *Isambard Kingdom Brunel*, Longman, 1957; Penguin, 1980

Index

Main entries are in bold type